THE GUGGENHEIM MEDALISTS

THE
GUGGENHEIM
MEDALISTS

ARCHITECTS OF THE AGE OF FLIGHT

THE GUGGENHEIM MEDALISTS
1929–1963

DANIEL GUGGENHEIM AND THE
AGE OF FLIGHT

THE DANIEL GUGGENHEIM MEDAL

BIOGRAPHICAL SKETCHES
THE GUGGENHEIM MEDALISTS

G. EDWARD PENDRAY, *EDITOR*

THE GUGGENHEIM MEDAL BOARD OF AWARD
OF THE UNITED ENGINEERING TRUSTEES, INC.
NEW YORK, 1964

THE DANIEL GUGGENHEIM MEDAL BOARD OF AWARD
1963

PUBLISHED BY

THE GUGGENHEIM MEDAL BOARD OF AWARD

OF THE UNITED ENGINEERING TRUSTEES, INC.

345 EAST 47TH STREET / NEW YORK 10017

PRICE: PAPER EDITION, TWO DOLLARS; CLOTH EDITION, THREE DOLLARS

CONTENTS

5

The Daniel Guggenheim Medal was established in 1927—and first granted in 1929—as an international award honoring those who have made great achievements in the advancement of flight.

The Medal also commemorates the personal encouragement and support given by Daniel Guggenheim to the development of flight, from 1925 until his death in 1930.

The Medal is of gold, and is awarded not more often than annually. There are no restrictions as to race, color, nationality or sex.

Provision for the Medal was made by a gift from the Daniel Guggenheim Fund for the Promotion of Aeronautics. The selection of recipients and the presentation of the Medal is administered by a Board of Award, composed of all living American recipients plus representatives of seven European countries and Canada, and three members each appointed by the American Society of Mechanical Engineers, the Society of Automotive Engineers and the American Institute of Aeronautics and Astronautics. The Board of Award is a committee of United Engineering Trustees, Inc., which manages the award funds. The General Manager and Secretary of United Engineering Trustees, Inc. serves as Secretary of the Board of Award.

THE GUGGENHEIM MEDALISTS
1929–1963

1929 ORVILLE WRIGHT: *For the design and construction, with his brother now deceased, of the first successful engine-propelled airplane.*

1930 LUDWIG PRANDTL: *For pioneer and creative work in the theory of dynamics.*

1931 FREDERICK WILLIAM LANCHESTER: *For contributions to the fundamental theory of aerodynamics.*

1932 JUAN DE LA CIERVA: *For development of the theory and practice of the Autogiro.*

1933 JEROME CLARKE HUNSAKER: *For contributions to the science of aerodynamics, to the science and art of aircraft design, and to the practical construction and utilization of rigid airships.*

1934 WILLIAM EDWARD BOEING: *For successful pioneering and achievement in aircraft manufacturing and air transport.*

1935 WILLIAM FREDERICK DURAND: *For notable achievement as pioneer in laboratory research and theory of aeronautics; distinguished contributions to the theory and development of aircraft propellers.*

1936 GEORGE WILLIAM LEWIS: *For pioneer and creative work in the theory of dynamics.*

1937 HUGO ECKENER: *For notable contributions to transoceanic air transport and to international cooperation in aeronautics.*

1938 SIR ROY FEDDEN: *For contributions to the development of aircraft engine design and for the specific design of the sleeve-valve aircraft engine.*

1939 DONALD WILLS DOUGLAS: *For outstanding contributions to the design and construction of transport airplanes.*

1940 GLENN LUTHER MARTIN: *For contributions to aeronautical development and the production of many types of aircraft of high performance.*

7

1941 JUAN TERRY TRIPPE: *For the development and successful operation of oceanic air transport.*

1942 JAMES HAROLD DOOLITTLE: *For notable achievements in the advancement of both the art and the science of aeronautics.*

1943 EDMUND TURNEY ALLEN: *For major contributions to aeronautics leading to important advances in airplane design, flight research, and airline operation; particularly for the presentation of new methods for operational control and for the development of scientific and systematic methods in the flight testing of aircraft for basic design and performance data.* (Posthumous)

1944 LAWRENCE DALE BELL: *For achievement in design and construction of military aircraft and for outstanding contributions to the methods of production.*

1945 THEODORE PAUL WRIGHT: *For outstanding contributions to the development of civil and military aircraft, and for notable achievement in assuring the success of our wartime aircraft production program.*

1946 SIR FRANK WHITTLE: *For pioneering the development of turbojet propulsion of aircraft.*

1947 LESTER DURAND GARDNER: *For outstanding achievement in advancing aeronautics, particularly for his conception and organization of the Institute of the Aeronautical Sciences.*

1948 LEROY RANDLE GRUMMAN: *For outstanding achievement in successfully advancing aircraft design, both for Naval and peacetime use.*

1949 EDWARD PEARSON WARNER: *For pioneering in research and a continuous record of contributions to the art and science of aeronautics.*

1950 HUGH LATIMER DRYDEN: *For outstanding leadership in aeronautical research and fundamental contributions to aeronautical science.*

1951 IGOR IVAN SIKORSKY: *For a lifetime of outstanding contributions to aeronautics, including pioneering with multi-engine airplanes, flying boats, amphibians and helicopters.*

1952   SIR GEOFFREY DE HAVILLAND: *For forty years of pioneering in military and commercial aircraft and the development of long-range jet transport.*

1953   CHARLES AUGUSTUS LINDBERGH: *For pioneering achievements in flight and air navigation.*

1954   CLARENCE DECATUR HOWE: *For initiating and organizing commercial air routes and services, promoting aeronautical research, development and production of aircraft and engines, and advancing the art of aeronautics.*

1955   THEODORE VON KÁRMÁN: *For long-continued leadership in the development of aerodynamic theory and its application to the practical problems of flight, in education in the aeronautical sciences, and in stimulating international cooperation in aeronautical research.*

1956   FREDERICK BRANT RENTSCHLER: *For a wide range of major achievements throughout a lifetime devoted to aviation, with specific reference to his many notable contributions to the vital aircraft engine field.* (Posthumous)

1957   ARTHUR EMMONS RAYMOND: *For the development of a long line of successful civil and military aircraft and for notable contributions to aeronautics in public service.*

1958   WILLIAM LITTLEWOOD: *For leadership and continuous personal participation over a quarter of a century in developing the equipment and operating techniques of air transport.*

1959   SIR GEORGE EDWARDS: *For a lifetime devoted to the design of military and commercial aircraft, culminating in the successful introduction into worldwide commercial service of the first turbine-powered propeller-driven aircraft.*

1960   GROVER LOENING: *For a lifetime devoted to the development of aeronautics in America.*

1961   JEROME LEDERER: *For his lifelong dedication to the cause of flight safety and his constant and untiring efforts to reduce the hazards of aviation.*

1962   JAMES HOWARD KINDELBERGER: *For technical and industrial leadership in producing excellent aircraft and space equipment, from early fighters to the X-15 space plane.* (Posthumous)

1963   JAMES SMITH MCDONNELL: *For lifetime contribution of outstanding nature in the design and development of military aircraft, and for pioneer work in space technology.*

DANIEL GUGGENHEIM 1856–1930

DANIEL GUGGENHEIM AND
THE AGE OF FLIGHT

Physically small, alert-eyed, quick and vigorous, a man of many interests and possessor of a sure grasp in practical matters, Daniel Guggenheim was second of the eight sons of Meyer Guggenheim, a Philadelphia business man and entrepreneur. Born in Philadelphia in 1856, Daniel's formal education ended at 17, when he was sent to take charge of the Swiss branch of a manufacturing and merchandising enterprise built up by his father. He returned to this country eleven years later, in 1884, to participate in another family venture: mining and smelting. He subsequently became one of the world's most famous capitalists and philanthropists. He died at Port Washington, Long Island, in 1930.

How much the age of flight owes to this prescient man, who never in his life owned an airplane or an airline, or in any other way stood to gain by the dawning aeronautical industry, will never be fully known. The objective facts of his participation can readily be stated. But what his intervention at a critical period really meant to aeronautical development in terms of years saved, new hope, restored enthusiasm, revitalized leadership, in the inspiration and enlistment of a whole new generation of men of flight and in the rousing of an apathetic public, can readily elude our present comprehension.

The fortune of Daniel Guggenheim came largely out of the earth; its benefits went in many directions. A philanthropist and patron in the grand manner, he believed and often quoted the traditional Hebrew proverb: "Who gives in health gives gold; in sickness, silver; after death, lead". During his lifetime he supported local and national charities, education, music and other arts, hospitals, medical, dental and social research, efforts toward the relief of human want and suffering on a world-wide scale, and forward-looking movements of many kinds. He not only gave money generously, but participated personally and actively in many of these projects as well. He was a tireless promoter of everything he considered good for progress and the enhancement of life.

His interest in aviation began almost by accident. When the United States entered the First World War, Daniel Guggenheim's two sons, Robert and Harry, promptly enlisted. The younger son, Harry—later American Ambassador to Cuba under President Hoover and famous in his own right for achievements in many fields— entered the war as a lieutenant in the Navy, serving as a naval aviator in the United States Aviation Forces in France, England and Italy. Commissioned a Lieutenant Commander in December 1918, he came home from the war deeply impressed by the possibilities of flying; especially peacetime aviation, which he felt might become one of the great forward surges in human development during his lifetime.

But it turned out that the period after the war was a time of troubles instead of progress for aviation. Surplus war planes were dumped on the market. Military airfields were deactivated; military flyers found themselves out of work. Determined to stick with the art that had given them so much satisfaction and excitement, some succeeded in making a precarious living by performing aerial circus stunts at carnivals and country fairs, wing-walking, parachute-jumping, taking passengers for short flights. A few were fortunate enough to get employment flying the mail, following the inauguration of air-mail lines by the United States Post Office in 1918. One or two passenger-carrying airlines had precariously sprung up in Europe, but there was none in this country. By the early '20's it had begun to appear that the development of aviation, once so hopeful, had become definitely stalled for lack of public interest and government support.

Young Harry Guggenheim was among those who watched with concern the failure of civil aviation to develop as anticipated. In the spring of 1925 he accepted an invitation to attend a meeting called by Chancellor Elmer Ellsworth Brown of New York University to consider ways of creating a School of Aeronautics in the University's College of Engineering. Present at the conference, in addition to the University head and Harry, were a couple of aviators, a battery of public relations experts, and Professor Alexander Klemin, who was teaching the few aeronautics courses then offered by the University and who had suggested the school.

A public campaign was proposed to raise half a million dollars. Harry dissented. "A campaign," he contended, "would be futile. At present the American people aren't much interested in aviation. They're likely to fear their money would be wasted." Asked for a counter-proposal, he suggested seeking out a single individual with vision and money enough to endow a school. He agreed to draft a letter for submission to a few such individuals, on condition that no members of his own family would be solicited.

He roughed out the letter that night. It so happened that he was spending it at Hempstead House, the Long Island mansion of Daniel Guggenheim. Before retiring Harry asked his father to criticize what he had written. The letter read, Daniel slipped it into the pocket of his dressing gown, saying, "Let me think about this overnight." At breakfast the next morning, "Well, Harry", he said, "I've thought about your letter and I've decided to endow the school myself." On June 15 Daniel's gift of $500,000 to the University was announced, and on the morning of Thursday, October 23, 1925, on the University's uptown campus at University Heights in the Bronx—he turned up a spadeful of earth on the site of the building that was to house the first School of Aeronautics in an American institution of higher learning.

"As I am an old man whose active days are past," Daniel said to the 400 or more faculty members, students and aviation pioneers gathered for the occasion, "I shall dedicate the rest of my life, with the active aid of my son, Harry F. Guggenheim, to the study and promotion of the science of aeronautics. I shall do this as a part of my duty to my country, whose ample opportunities have ever been at my hand and whose bountiful blessings I have had the good fortune to enjoy."

Establishment of this school won a surprising amount of acclaim. Newspapers featured it from coast to coast. Chancellor Brown wrote Mr. Guggenheim: "You have taken a step which will enable us to render a national service in a field of engineering now but scantily provided with a means of study". The gift, he said, had made possible "immense benefits to mankind, opening the door to careers which promise benefit to our people no less than... other branches of science and engineering."

13

DANIEL GUGGENHEIM AND CHANCELLOR ELMER E. BROWN AT
GROUND-BREAKING CEREMONIES FOR THE DANIEL GUGGENHEIM
SCHOOL OF AERONAUTICS, NEW YORK UNIVERSITY.

For Daniel and Harry Guggenheim the founding of The Guggenheim School of Aeronautics at New York University was only a beginning. Before long, Daniel was deep in further and more ambitious plans to hasten the development of flight, especially its peacetime aspects. Both men had become convinced that the real future of aviation lay in commercial passenger transportation; that something must be done to demonstrate that passenger traffic by air was safe, practical, and commercially feasible. Between them they developed a bold new plan for approaching the job.

The new proposal was carefully explored by Harry at a meeting with President Coolidge in the latter part of 1925, in the Executive Offices in Washington. To the meeting the President invited the then Secretary of Commerce, Herbert Hoover. The discussion went on for some time, at length adjourning to the President's study. President Coolidge was favorably impressed.

As a result, on January 16, 1926, Daniel Guggenheim wrote a letter to Secretary Hoover, in which he announced the establishment of the Daniel Guggenheim Fund for the Promotion of Aeronautics. The initial grant was $500,000, to which he later added $2,000,000, and still later another $500,000. The purposes of the Fund were outlined as follows:

1. To promote aeronautical education both in institutions of learning and among the general public.
2. To assist in the extension of fundamental aeronautical science.
3. To assist in the development of commercial aircraft and aircraft equipment.
4. To further the application of aircraft in business, industry and other economic and social activities of the nation.

"I have confidence that the Fund can serve an important purpose," wrote Daniel. "Recent events in the United States have stimulated much discussion of aviation.* The time is ripe for action. There is urgent need in our country for immediate, practical

* This was a reference to headlines being made at this time by Brigadier General William "Billy" Mitchell, who had commanded U.S. Air Forces in France during the war, was demanding an independent air arm, and buttressing his proposal with attacks on Army and Navy leaders for what he called their "neglect of air power." He was soon to be demoted and court martialed for his pains.

and substantial assistance to aviation in its commercial, industrial and scientific aspects. No less urgent is the need to awaken the American public, especially our business men, to the advantages and possibilities of commercial aircraft—in a word, to make the American public in a very real sense, 'air-wise'."

History contains a number of examples of relatively small investments which, coming at just the right time and entrusted to just the right hands, produced spectacular results: the investment of Queen Isabella in the westward voyage of Columbus; the purchase of Manhattan from the Indians for $24; the $2,400 provided by Congress for the Lewis and Clark Expedition. In terms of what it was to mean for the advancement of flight at this critical time, the investment of encouragement, money and guidance provided by Daniel Guggenheim was to be of an order perhaps not too far removed from these.

2

Harry F. Guggenheim, then 36, became President of the Fund. The original Board of Trustees included Rear Admiral Hutchinson I. Cone, the first Vice President of the Fund and later head of the U.S. Shipping Board; F. Trubee Davison, then Assistant Secretary of War for Air; Dwight W. Morrow, Senator, man of affairs, and destined to become the father-in-law of Charles Lindbergh; Elihu Root, Jr., well-known lawyer, and John D. Ryan, a powerful figure in the world of finance. Later additions included Orville Wright; Major General George W. Goethals, builder of the Panama Canal; Professor William F. Durand, educator and aeronautical engineer; Dr. Robert A. Millikan, winner of the Nobel Prize for physics and President of California Institute of Technology; and Professor Albert A. Michelson, physicist and Nobel prize winner. In June 1928 Captain, later Vice Admiral, Emory S. Land, of the Construction Corps of the U.S. Navy, became Vice President, succeeding Admiral Cone upon his appointment to the Shipping Board.

The first task of the Fund was to determine how to approach its problem, and where. Since some aspects of the commercial use of aircraft had been moving ahead faster in Europe than in this country, it was decided that Harry Guggenheim and Admiral Cone would visit England, France, Germany, Holland, Italy and Spain,

HARRY F. GUGGENHEIM, WHEN PRESIDENT OF THE DANIEL GUGGENHEIM
FUND FOR THE PROMOTION OF AERONAUTICS.

interviewing leading aeronautical authorities and visiting the principal centers of aviation, aeronautical research and education.

At sea on the return voyage, Harry Guggenheim wrote a report on what had been seen and heard, noting among other things that aeronautical education was no further advanced in Europe than in the United States; that aeronautical engineers and pilots abroad were meeting the same difficulties as in the United States in finding employment, but that research, especially in England, had made some progress toward the solution of the problems of stability in flight. The investigators found few laboratories fully equipped for aeronautical research, but had been greatly impressed by Professor Ludwig Prandtl's research organization and establishment at Goettingen, Germany, probably the foremost then in existence.

The report presented figures showing that passenger transport had been making progress in Europe, and disclosed an interesting paradox: a good proportion of the passengers were not native Europeans, but Americans, mostly tourists. This particular discovery gave the President of the fund encouragement to believe that Americans could be brought to take to the air in their own country as well, if facilities were available.

"Finally, but far from least in importance," the report concluded, "Europe today is far ahead of the United States in the number of able men, both in and out of government service, who are devoting their lives to the solution of the problems confronting civil aviation."

Spurred by these findings, the Fund at once began a multi-faceted attack upon the problems of civil aviation in the United States, and rapidly brought into its orbit a number of men who were later to become leading figures in the swiftly unfolding story of human flight.

From the beginning, the Fund had conceived its principal objectives as falling into two general categories, immediate and long range. Among its immediate problems the Fund included "giving the pilot eyes": that is, enabling him to fly and land his craft in any kind of weather or fog conditions; demonstrating a practical passenger airline in operation, promoting and demonstrating aircraft safety, and "popularizing" flight.

Among its long-range objectives were the establishment of special schools or departments of aeronautics; fundamental research in aeronautics, aircraft design and engineering; promotion of safety as a long-range continuing program as well as for the short term, and the need to point out and honor unusual aeronautical achievement as a means of stimulating more of it.

Programs in each of these categories were put under way rapidly, spurred by the continuing sharp interest of Daniel Guggenheim and the energetic approaches and enthusiasm of Harry.

To deal with fog and weather, the Fund established, in September 1927, the Daniel Guggenheim Committee on Aeronautical Meteorology. This Committee was itself the outgrowth of an earlier, 1926, committee composed of the President of the Fund and the three then Assistant United States Secretaries for Air of the War, the Navy, and Commerce Departments: F. Trubee Davison, Edward P. Warner and William P. MacCracken, Jr. The object of both committees was to pursue research on fog dissipation, means of locating flying fields from the air regardless of weather, instruments which would show accurately the height of an airplane above the ground, instruments and techniques for flying in fog, and means of penetrating fog by light rays.

It soon became evident that this bundle of problems was altogether too large to be undertaken all at once, or by any single group. Flying and landing in fog was therefore singled out for special attention, and a new organization, the Full Flight Laboratory, was set up. Headquarters of the Full Flight Laboratory were at Mitchel Field, Long Island, New York, made available by the Army Air Corps.

The man selected to spearhead this operation was Lieutenant, later Lieutenant General, James H. Doolittle, destined to become world-famous for his flying exploits, which included leadership of the first bombing raid on Tokyo from an aircraft carrier in World War II. At the Full Flight Laboratory, Lieutenant Doolittle was to demonstrate fully the remarkable Doolittle brand of courage, energy, insight and organizing ability, combined with high technical understanding and superb flying skill.*

Flying in fog, bad enough at any time, was an exceedingly dangerous procedure before the development of cockpit instruments to inform the pilot of his altitude,

* In these operations Professor William Brown of the Massachusetts Institute of Technology was Technical Assistant to Lieutenant Doolittle, and Lieutenant, later Brigadier General, Benjamin Kelsey served as check or safety pilot.

REAR ADMIRAL H. I. CONE, FIRST VICE PRESIDENT OF THE
GUGGENHEIM FUND, LATER HEAD OF THE U.S. SHIPPING BOARD.
CAPTAIN (LATER VICE ADMIRAL) EMORY S. LAND, WHO SUCCEEDED
REAR ADMIRAL CONE AS VICE PRESIDENT OF THE FUND.

speed and position in the absence of visual contact with the ground or horizon. The task of the Full Flight Laboratory was not merely to investigate fundamental problems, but to promote the development of needed instruments and work out necessary techniques, and demonstrate the effectiveness of both in such a manner as to prove beyond doubt that flying and landing in fog was both possible and practical.

The first problem was to develop an instrument much·better than the existing turn-and-bank indicator; one that would clearly inform the pilot of his position relative to the horizon, assisting him to keep his aircraft in level flight when the natural horizon was not visible. The Fund requested two industrial companies to undertake this development. Within a relatively short time one of them, the Sperry Gyroscope Company, produced a practical artificial-horizon that gave direct indication of both lateral and longitudinal attitude of the aircraft with respect to the natural horizon.

The second problem was development of some type of compass that would give the pilot a correct indication of the extent of his turn, in either direction, instantaneously and under all conditions of flight. Neither the magnetic compass nor the earth inductor compass then in use could do this. The Fund again asked commercial companies to cooperate in this development. The Sperry Company shortly complied with a suitable instrument, the directional gyro.

The third lack was an instrument that would give a pilot accurate indication of his altitude above the surface of the ground. Altimeters then available, based on barometric pressure, gave a reading only of altitude above sea level, provided the barometric pressure was known, and even so were not sufficiently sensitive. For the third time the Fund turned to industrial companies for help. The Kollsman Instrument Company soon was able to refine the barometer altimeter to give a reading of altitude to within ten feet. For the time and purpose, this was a major advance.

These instruments covered the essentials for blind flying, but for blind landing still another aid was required: a means of directing the pilot toward the airport and bringing him on an accurate course toward the landing spot, indicating the correct glide path and the aircraft's location with relation to the runway and the edge of the field.

Mitchel Field already had in use a standard army aural-type radio beacon with a satisfactory range of 100 miles, but it did not meet the needs of the final landing approach. The Fund asked the cooperation of the National Bureau of Standards and

Courtesy Sperry Gyroscope Company

LIEUTENANT (NOW LIEUTENANT GENERAL) JAMES H. DOOLITTLE IN THE
HOODED COCKPIT IN WHICH HE DEMONSTRATED THE FEASIBILITY OF
INSTRUMENT FLYING, SEPTEMBER 24, 1929, AT MITCHEL FIELD, NEW YORK.

the Department of Commerce in the construction of an additional short-range visual-type beacon, which could be moved when necessary to any part of the landing area. The two beacons, used together, were considered sufficient to keep the pilot on correct course during approach and when coming in to land.

Two planes were provided by the Fund for the experiments in blind flying: a Consolidated NY-2 military training plane with a Wright J-5 engine, and a Vought Corsair 02U-1 with a Pratt and Whitney Wasp engine. Lieutenant Doolittle used both, in numerous skillfully-executed tests. On one hazardous cross-country flight, from Buffalo to New York in March 1929, he was forced to make a crash landing in fog near Elizabeth, New Jersey, and washed out the 02U-1. Fortunately Lieutenant Doolittle was uninjured. The Fund promptly replaced the crashed plane.

These intensive efforts came to fruition on September 24, 1929, just two years after the formation of the Committee on Aeronautical Meteorology, and almost exactly one year after Lieutenant Doolittle became head of the Full Flight Laboratory. An announcement by Harry Guggenheim that day declared: "As a result of tests successfully conducted this morning at Mitchel Field, the Daniel Guggenheim Fund for the Promotion of Aeronautics is able to report a solution of the hitherto unsolved last phase in the problem of flying through fog. Under conditions representing the densest fog, reaching from any altitude to the ground, Lieutenant James H. Doolittle, conducting the experiment, was able to take off from the airport, fly from it and return to a given spot and make a landing."

What Lieutenant Doolittle did was to take off from Mitchel Field in a completely hooded cockpit, flying by instrument only. He flew away from the field, turned around and recrossed it, turned 180 degrees again, came back and landed a short distance from his starting point—all without visual contact with horizon, sky or field.

Years later, in his Lester Gardner Lecture in 1961 on "Early Blind Flying", Doolittle commented on this exploit: "Actually, despite previous practice, the final approach and landing were sloppy. This entire flight was made under the hood in a completely covered cockpit which had been carefully sealed to keep out all light. The flight, from takeoff to landing, lasted fifteen minutes. It was the first time an airplane had been taken off, flown over a set course and landed by instruments alone. This was just ten months and three weeks from the first test flight of the NY-2."

23

LIEUTENANT DOOLITTLE AND HARRY GUGGENHEIM READY FOR A FLIGHT IN ONE OF THE PLANES OF THE FULL FLIGHT LABORATORY.

"Sloppy" or no, it was a dramatic, truly remarkable demonstration of the prodigies that could be accomplished in a short time, in a highly technical area, through good organization and teamwork, the cooperation of industry and government, and the unflinching courage of an unusual man. Since that day instrument flying has been accepted as a matter of course.

3

Most aircraft in use in 1926 were either military planes or craft designed along military lines; in which speed, load-carrying capacity or maneuverability in flight were primary considerations. To assure a basis for commercial passenger use, the airplane would also have to be provided with inherent safety in flying and landing.

Some interesting attempts to design safer planes had been made in Europe. Juan de la Cierva's Autogiro had experienced a modest success, but had practical drawbacks. There was an experimental plane called the Pterodactyl, a tailless craft produced by G. T. R. Hill in England. The Handley Page slotted wing showed promise, and indicated that much could be done to improve stability and safety in conventional airplanes.

The truth was, however, that few manufacturers and designers either in this country or abroad appeared to be sufficiently emphasizing safety. In mid-June of 1926 the Fund issued a statement, drafted by Harry Guggenheim, which declared: "The primary reason for the slow development of aviation in this country and for its unsatisfactory financial status in those countries where, through government subsidies, air lines are established, would seem to be lack of public confidence in flying. The success of commercial aviation should be evinced not by statistics, but by actual demonstration that airplanes are inherently no more dangerous than steamships or railroads."

This was followed by an announcement that the Fund would appropriate $150,000 to $200,000 to encourage endeavors in this country and abroad to make the airplane safe, through a formally organized Safe Aircraft Competition which would be open to airplane manufacturers in any part of the world.

Then came a period of discussion on suitable rules for the contest. The Fund wished to require real achievement by the winner of the top award; yet did not want to encourage the development of freak or impractical craft designed only for the purpose of winning. A rules drafting group was set up, consisting of Harry Guggenheim, Admiral Cone and the three technical advisors for the Competition: Major R. H. Mayo, Professor Alexander Klemin, and Lieutenant E. E. Aldrin, aided and advised by a series of aeronautical experts. Among the personalities who participated were Anthony H. G. Fokker, airplane designer and flyer; Charles Day, an old-timer who had built a famous airplane, the Standard, before the War; Major R. W. Schroeder, then holder of the world's altitude record for aircraft and who was later advisor to the Bureau of Air Commerce; Lieutenant James H. Doolittle; J. D. Hill, a well-known veteran flyer and airmail pilot; G. M. Bellanca, aircraft designer, and Edward P. Warner, Assistant Secretary of the Navy for Aeronautics.

The rules were finally ready for publication in April 1927. Announcement that the Safe Aircraft Competition was formally open came at a dinner in New York a few days later. Harry Guggenheim declared its objective to be "to achieve a real advance in the safety of flying through improvement in the aerodynamic characteristics of heavier-than-air craft, without sacrificing the good practical qualities of the present-day aircraft."

To qualify, an entry would have to comply with normal structural strength requirements, have a satisfactory power plant, show a maximum speed of not less than 110 miles per hour, a climb rate of at least 400 feet per minute, a useful load-carrying capacity of 5 pounds per horsepower, endurance indicated by ability to fly three hours at full power, full normal instrument equipment, adequate space for the useful load, adequate vision for the pilot, and all reasonable precautions against risks of fire. Each entry was to pass all of these preliminary requirements before it would be permitted to make the final tests.

The final tests included demonstration of minimum speed in level flight of not more than 35 miles per hour; minimum steady gliding speed under full control of not more than 38 miles per hour; ability to come to rest within 100 feet after first touching ground; ability to glide in over an obstruction 35 feet high and come to rest within a distance of 300 feet from the base of the obstruction; ability to take off after a run of not more than 300 feet from a standing start and clear an obstruction 35 feet high at a distance of 500 feet from the starting point; ability to glide in a steady-flight path at an angle of not more than 8 degrees to the horizontal; ability to glide at an angle of not less than 16 degrees to the horizontal, and ability to demonstrate stability, maneuverability and effective controllability under all normal conditions. The test considered most important was that of ability to land in a confined space.

Each of the first five competitors to satisfy all of the requirements was to receive a "safety prize" of $10,000. The top winner of the Competition was to receive the main prize of $100,000, which would include the safety prize if previously awarded. Entries sent great distances were also to receive special grants on the basis of a dollar a mile in excess of 1,000 miles, up to a maximum grant of $2,000 for any contestant. The purpose of these special grants was, of course, to encourage competitors from the far west and Europe.

The opening date for receiving entries was September 1, 1927. Entries were finally to be closed two years later, on September 1, 1929.

On the opening day, five British firms announced that they planned to enter. Entries soon began to come also from manufacturers in the United States. In all, twenty-seven entries were received:

United States   Bourdon Aircraft Corporation
Brunner-Winkle Aircraft Corporation
V. J. Burnelli
Command-Aire, Inc.
Cosmic Aircraft Corporation
Cunningham-Hall Aircraft Corporation
Curtiss Aeroplane & Motor Company, Inc.
Dare Airplane Company
Fleet Aircraft, Inc.
Ford-Leigh Safety Wing, Inc.
Gates Aircraft Corporation
Charles Ward Hall, Inc.
Heraclio Alfaro
J. S. McDonnell, Jr., & Associates

THE CURTISS TANAGER CLIMBING OVER THE 35-FOOT BARRIER, STARTING 500 FEET FROM THE BASE OF THE OBSTACLE, IN FINAL TESTS OF THE SAFE AIRCRAFT COMPETITION.

Moth Aircraft Corporation
Pitcairn-Cierva Autogiro Company of America
Rocheville Aircraft Corporation
Schroeder-Wentworth Company
Taylor Brothers Aircraft Corporation
Whittelsey Manufacturing Company
John H. Wiggins Company, Inc.

Great Britain   Cierva Aircraft Company
de Havilland Aircraft Company, Ltd.
Gloster Aircraft Company, Ltd.
Handley Page, Ltd.
Vickers, Ltd.

Italy   Società Italiana Ernesta Breda

The organization set up to conduct the Competition included eighteen persons, of whom six composed the Committee of Judges: Orville Wright, F. Trubee Davison, Edward P. Warner, William P. McCracken, Jr., Rear Admiral Richard E. Byrd, and Dr. George W. Lewis. Technical advisors were Professor Alexander Klemin, Major E. E. Aldrin, and Major R. H. Mayo. The field manager was Captain Walter Bender, and the test pilots were E. W. Rounds, Thomas Carroll, and Lieutenant Stanley Umstead.

In the end, fifteen airplanes appeared at Mitchel Field late in 1929 for the testing. Of these, three withdrew without tests; two were damaged in preliminary flying.

Entries finally taking part in the Competition included one from Great Britain by Handley Page, Ltd., and nine from the United States, by Bourdon Aircraft Corporation, V. J. Burnelli, Command-Aire, Inc., Cunningham-Hall Aircraft Corporation, Curtiss Aeroplane & Motor Company, Inc., Fleet Aircraft, Inc., Ford-Leigh Safety Wing, Inc., Schroeder-Wentworth Company, and Taylor Brothers Aircraft Corporation.

Two craft gave by far the best performances: the Handley Page and the Curtiss.

Both were biplanes; the Handley Page an open cockpit design; the Curtiss a cabin plane. Each was equipped with anti-stall wing slots and trailing-edge flaps which acted as brakes either in flight or landing. The Curtiss plane was also fitted with floating-type ailerons at the wing tips. It was called the Tanager, and was designed and constructed by a Curtiss team headed by Dr. Theodore P. Wright, at that time Chief Engineer of the Airplane Division of the Curtiss Aeroplane & Motor Company; later Administrator of Civil Aeronautics, Vice President of Cornell University in charge of research, President of the Cornell Aeronautical Laboratory, and Chairman of the Executive Committee of the Daniel and Florence Guggenheim Aviation Safety Center at Cornell.

The Handley Page was a close second all during the Competition, but the Curtiss Tanager was the only entry that handily passed all requirements and reached the stage for "awarded points".

"I well remember the exciting two-and-a-half year period starting in May, 1927, with the announcement of a Safe Aircraft Competition", Dr. Wright recalled in 1963, in a private memorandum on his experiences in the Competition. "Many recollections crowd my mind: the design conferences, the wind tunnel tests, the manufacturing problems, many details of design, our own flight tests and those of the Fund's pilots.

"There were three sets of flight tests conducted by the Fund's pilots. First came the qualifying tests, and here none of the entries based on then-current designs, even with considerable modification, could qualify by a wide margin. Then the so-called safety requirements were checked in flight, and finally, rating tests were conducted to determine scoring points for achievement in performance better than the qualifying minimums.

"The design features which contributed most to the success of the Curtiss Tanager were the automatic, interconnected slots and flaps located over the whole wing span, made possible by the use of wing tip floating ailerons, a most important innovation. In addition to this essential feature, the floating ailerons gave the aircraft superb lateral control, with no adverse yawing moment, throughout the whole flight regime. It was, of course, necessary to achieve refinement of design in all components of the Tanager to obtain required light weight, low drag and structural integrity.

"The flight tests demonstrated a minimum gliding speed of 37 miles per hour and flying speed of 30.6 miles per hour; high speed of 111.6 miles per hour; take-off distance of 295 feet and distance of 500 feet to clear a 35-foot barrier; and landing run of 90 feet, with a total distance to stop from a 35-foot obstacle of 293 feet."

Presentation of the first prize of $100,000 to the Curtiss Aeroplane & Motor Company was made on January 6, 1930. The award was made by Captain Emory S. Land, Vice President of the Fund. At the ceremonies he said:

"Officials of the Fund have always felt that the intangible results of the Safe Aircraft Competition would be far greater than the tangible results. We still feel that way. This competition has initiated development throughout the aviation world. This will continue for years to come. The seed planted by this competition will bear fruit for the next decade. The aviation world owes a debt of gratitude to Mr. Daniel Guggenheim."

During the flight tests, Daniel Guggenheim was a frequent visitor at Mitchel Field, and he watched the flying with absorbed interest. Though his age at the time was 73, his eyes and mind were still on the future. In a published statement he declared:

"We must realize that the air age is already here. Once realized, our provincialism will fall away from us. Universal flying will make all of us neighbors, and as sure as the steamboat and railroad are universal, the airplane will be."

4

The Fund's first opportunity to begin "popularizing" flying, one of its principal objectives, came early, and helped to set a new pattern of activity thereafter carried on simultaneously with its more technical endeavors. The popularizing program began early in 1926, when Harry Guggenheim conceived the idea of Fund-sponsored Air Tours, which would permit the public to see and hear famous flyers and their aircraft and witness demonstrations of flying skill.

Shortly after midnight on May 9, 1926, Commander Richard E. Byrd, in the *Josephine Ford*, a three-engined Fokker airplane piloted by Floyd Bennett, took off on skis from a runway at King's Bay, Spitzbergen, and made a spectacular round-trip

THE JOSEPHINE FORD ON HER GUGGENHEIM TOUR.

flight over the North Pole, returning sixteen hours later to world acclaim for this daring exploit. When Byrd and Bennett came back to the United States during the summer, they were promptly invited to undertake the first of the proposed Air Tours of principal cities in the United States.

Commander Byrd readily assented, but was unable to make the tour himself because of previous commitments. Floyd Bennett agreed to go, and a Tour in the *Josephine Ford*, including stops at some 40 cities, was arranged. Bernt Balchen, distinguished pioneer pilot in his own right, accompanied Bennett on the Tour as second pilot. Other members of the party were Donald Keyhoe as manager, and Charles F. Kunkel as Fund representative.

The Tour started from Washington, D.C., on October 7, 1926, making its first stop at Mitchel Field. It adhered closely to schedule; only one unexpected incident developed. At Cheyenne, Wyoming, the *Josephine Ford* was snowbound for a day, necessitating some changes in the subsequent itinerary and timetable. The plane and party returned to Bolling Field, Washington, on November 23. Harry Guggenheim celebrated its return in these words:

"I think it a remarkable demonstration of the advances already made in aviation that the same plane which carried Commander Byrd and Pilot Bennett over the North Pole is able to complete a swing around the country with no more difficulty than would be found in a motor trip over present-day good roads."

The Tour a year later by Colonel Charles A. Lindbergh, just following his trans-Atlantic flight, was the one however which really broke through public apathy and opened the mind of the average citizen to the possibilities of air travel.

The famous flyer had already known a good deal about the Fund when he arrived at Curtiss Field in May 1927 to begin his trans-Atlantic flight.

"I first heard about it when I was a mail pilot on the St. Louis-Chicago route," he recalled recently. "I remember clearly being impressed by the fact that a great foundation had been established to encourage the development of aviation. I believe one of the more important results from the establishment of the Daniel Guggenheim Fund, certainly one of the most immediate results, lay in the confidence it implied in civil aviation in those early years, and in the respectability it gave the profession.

"The announcement of a multi-million dollar fund, created by a successful and

respected businessman, had an extraordinary effect on morale and went far in sup-
porting the claims of those of us who believed that the airplane had a brilliant future."

Harry Guggenheim and Lindbergh met for the first time at Curtiss Field while
Lindbergh was preparing for his Paris flight. Just before the takeoff, Harry said:
"Look me up when you get back." Lindbergh did, and was invited for an indefinite
visit and rest at Falaise, Harry Guggenheim's home at Port Washington, Long Island.
There he wrote his description of his flight in the book "We". On June 28, 1927,
the Fund announced that Colonel Lindbergh would undertake a Flight Tour of
the country "for the primary purpose of stimulating popular interest in the use of
air transport."

"It will enable millions of people who have had an opportunity only to read and
hear about the Colonel's remarkable achievement to see him and his plane in action",
the announcement declared. "It is our belief that such an expedition... will strike the
air-consciousness of the American people and give added impetus to commercial
flying as a practical, safe, and useful means of transportation."

Since Colonel Lindbergh's plane, the *Spirit of St. Louis*, was only a single-seater, it
was arranged that another plane, piloted by Philip R. Love and furnished by the
Department of Commerce, would accompany it. Strictly on schedule, the Tour
began on July 20, less than two months after the trans-Atlantic flight. A careful itinerary had been worked out with the help of Colonel Lindbergh. It would involve going
to all 48 states, including 23 state capitals. A total of 82 stops were to be made, of
which 13 would be brief "touch" stops and 69 would be longer stops, with ceremonies and speeches.

The performance was notable for its efficiency. City after city saw Lindbergh and
his plane, and had its parade and ceremonies, viewed the *Spirit of St. Louis* as it de-
parted again, each visit strictly conforming to the timetable. The Colonel and his
plane were scheduled to arrive at precisely 12:00 noon at each stop, and all arrivals in
fact took place with great precision. It was Colonel Lindbergh who insisted on strict
adherence to the program, to prove the dependability and reliability of flying. In only
one instance was there a departure from the plan. Thick fog at Portland, Maine, an
early stop on the tour, caused a delay in arrival, but did not affect the rest of the Tour.

In each city Colonel Lindbergh went through a heavy program of receptions, wel-

THE LINDBERGH PARTY ON THE GUGGENHEIM TOUR. LEFT TO RIGHT:
DONALD E. KEYHOE, OF THE DEPARTMENT OF COMMERCE, AIDE TO
COLONEL LINDBERGH; PHILIP R. LOVE, PILOT OF THE
ACCOMPANYING PLANE; COLONEL LINDBERGH; C. C. MAIDMENT, SERVICE
REPRESENTATIVE; MILBURN KUSTERER, ADVANCE REPRESENTATIVE.

COLONEL CHARLES A. LINDBERGH LANDING AT OMAHA, NEBRASKA, IN THE SPIRIT OF ST. LOUIS ON THE GUGGENHEIM TOUR.

comes, meetings, dinners, addresses. He himself made a total of 147 speeches, mostly dwelling on the future of flying, the need to develop airports, the safety and reliability of aviation, the possibilities of passenger service by air. In many cities where stops were not scheduled, Colonel Lindbergh flew over and dropped a message of greeting signed by himself, Harry Guggenheim and W. P. McCracken, Jr., Assistant Secretary for Aeronautics of the Department of Commerce.

In all, the *Spirit of St. Louis* flew 260 hours on the Tour, covering 22,350 miles without a mishap or delay of any kind except the brief one at Portland. Lindbergh attended 69 dinners, paraded 1,285 miles, and was seen and heard by an estimated 30,000,000 persons. At the end he was invited to join the Fund as a member and trustee. He also became a consultant to the Fund, and one of his suggestions in this capacity was to provide an unexpected benefit from the Tour.

Colonel Lindbergh had noted, in flying over the then 48 states of the Union, that very few cities, towns and communities could be identified from the air. He suggested that it would be of great value to have roof markings as an aid in guiding pilots in cross-country flights. The Fund, acting on the suggestion, issued a statement in October 1928 asking all towns and cities with populations between 1,000 and 50,000 to identify themselves by suitable roof markings.

"Believing that such identification is a first essential for an air transportation system," the announcement continued, "the Fund has organized a nation-wide campaign for this purpose, in which the Departments of War, Navy, Commerce and the Post Office are cooperating."

With the endorsement of the Postmaster General, the Fund asked postmasters throughout the country to take the initiative in identifying their communities by means of adequate roof markings. In a printed bulletin it described the type of roof most suitable for marking, and urged the use of block letters in chrome yellow with a black background, the letters to be ten to twenty feet high. The name of the town was to be accompanied by an arrow pointing due north with the letter "N" over it, and a smaller arrow indicating the direction of the local airport, if there were one.

The preliminary appeal to postmasters was followed by similar appeals to major industries and various organizations. Oil companies and railroads, as well as many businesses, civic organizations and service clubs, joined the campaign. Edsel Ford, then President of the Ford Motor Company, arranged with Ford's 7,600 dealers in all parts of the country to participate.

Fewer than 2,000 towns and communities had rooftops marked for identification from the air when the campaign began. By December 31, 1929, fourteen months later, more than 8,000 towns and communities had been so identified. The group or person responsible for placing a marker in each town received a certificate of appreciation signed by Colonel Lindbergh. A total of 7,800 of these were awarded.

5

During the whole life of the Fund, Daniel Guggenheim was accustomed to drop in at the offices to talk over its various projects with Harry, Admiral Cone, Captain Land and others. Out of his broad experience, his shrewd ability to size up a situation and push for practical solutions, came useful ideas for further and faster progress. Daniel did not pretend to understand the technology involved in the numerous programs of the Fund, but he did comprehend the importance of sticking to main objectives and getting the job done.

In 1927 he began to inquire increasingly what the Fund was planning to do about demonstrating a successful airline in commercial operation, a project he included among the most significant it could undertake.

After considerable discussion, it was decided to call a meeting of all air-mail contractors in the country, to discuss ways and means of adding passenger traffic to their enterprises. To assure good attendance it was necessary in some cases to accompany the invitation with a railroad ticket; the air-mail business was both precarious and unremunerative, and some operators felt they could not afford to attend at their own expense.

The meeting was hardly a success. The idea of establishing passenger airlines was almost unanimously rejected. Some operators asserted with candor that merely carrying the mail by air could not be profitable without a subsidy, and passenger service without a subsidy would mean financial disaster. Others thought there inevitably would be accidents, which might react unfavorably on the airmail business as well.

Only two operators, Harris M. Hansue and Walter T. Varney, showed any interest in the proposal.

The meeting further made it clear, that few, if any, mail route operators were in financial condition to afford the equipment necessary to start a passenger airline, even if otherwise willing. In considering how this might be overcome, Harry Guggenheim recalled the system of equipment loans so successfully used in the early days of the railroads and street car lines. A study of equipment loans was made for the Fund; it was concluded that they could be applied in the case of air transport.

Once more the Fund held a meeting of air transport authorities and airmail operators. This time there was more interest. The Fund promptly made a public announcement: it would offer equipment loans for passenger airlines, open to any applicant who could meet the requirements.

"The loans will be made only to existing operating companies for the purchase of the most modern, multi-engined planes of maximum safety and comfort, so that an actual demonstration of performance and safety will be available as an incentive for further development of passenger air lines in the United States," said the announcement.

"Planes bought under the equipment-loan provision must be designed to fly should one of the motors be disabled. The route or routes over which the new equipment will be flown must be approved for passenger-carrying by the Aeronautical Division of the Department of Commerce."

A short time later, on October 4, 1927, the Fund disclosed that Western Air Express, operating between Los Angeles and San Francisco, had applied for and had been granted the first equipment loan. The route of Western Air Express, of which Harris M. Hansue was President and General Manager, had been surveyed jointly by the Fund and the Department of Commerce, and found practical for the proposed model passenger air line. Western Air Express agreed to establish service early in 1928, on a regular three-hour daylight schedule.

Mr. Hanshue issued a statement in which he explained: "The air-line distance between Los Angeles and San Francisco is 365 miles and the time necessary for flight over this route will be approximately three hours. Planes will leave either terminal at 10:30 o'clock in the morning, and will arrive at the other terminal at

1:30 o'clock in the afternoon. Airports in both cities are situated within thirty minutes from the business sections so that office-to-office movements may be completed within four hours, as compared with the $13^1/_2$ hours now required by railroad.

"This arrangement... will permit business men in either city to attend their offices in the morning, disposing of important details, and then leave for the airport to keep two-o'clock afternoon appointments in the other city. By combining this service with return by fast night trains the round trip can be completed in a period of twenty-four hours.

"Western Air Express will provide the latest conveniences for its passengers on this air line. Lunch will be served in the air, and magazines, the latest editions of newspapers and radio entertainment and market reports will be available."

Thus, even before the pioneer American airline had begun operation, some of the principal sales appeals and flight customs of modern airlines had been established.

Three planes for the pioneer line were chosen after much study and consideration, participated in not only by Mr. Hanshue and his associates but also by Harry Guggenheim, Colonel Lindbergh, C. S. "Casey" Jones and others. They were ten passenger tri-motored Fokker F-10s, equipped with Pratt & Whitney 400-horse-power engines. The guaranteed maximum speed was 140 miles per hour, and the cruising speed at least 120 miles per hour. The manufacturer guaranteed that the reserve of power would be sufficient to keep these planes flying full load, even with one engine dead. The price was $50,000 each.

The Fund authorized the airline to purchase the planes direct from the manufacturer. The loan of $150,000 was to be repaid over a period of two years, at five per cent interest. During the two-year period Western Air Express was to assign its ownership of the aircraft to the Fund, and also put up securities in a bank to protect the Fund in case of damage to the planes. On completion of the payments, the planes were to become the property of Western Air Express.

The new passenger airline went into service in May 1928. From the start it was a success. Passengers took to it promptly; the income from traffic enabled Western Air Express to repay the Fund's loan in the time specified. So effective was the demonstration that no further equipment loans from the Fund were required. Other passenger airlines began to spring up almost at once in various parts of the country, and

Courtesy American Institute of Aeronautics and Astronautics

ONE OF THE FOKKER TRIMOTORED PLANES BUILT FOR
WESTERN AIR EXPRESS AND PURCHASED THROUGH A
GUGGENHEIM FUND EQUIPMENT LOAN. THESE PLANES INAUGURATED
REGULAR AIRLINE PASSENGER SERVICE IN THE UNITED STATES.

within a short time airlines were to constitute one of the nation's principal forms of transport.

6

Even on the West Coast, the uncertainties of the weather continued to be a menacing obstacle to the further progress of the air age.

The Fund's Meteorological Committee had given much study to weather and the airplane. One of the results was the conclusion that ordinary weather forecasting services then available, though perhaps sufficient for agriculture and the other purposes for which they had been developed, were quite inadequate to serve the coming age of flight. The Committee proposed setting up a model weather service designed specifically for servicing a passenger airline.

After considering a number of routes, the Committee selected the Western Air Express line, already carefully studied in connection with the equipment loan. On June 3, 1928, the Fund announced the installation on the Los Angeles-San Francisco airway of a "complete weather-reporting service", in cooperation with the U.S. Weather Bureau, the Department of Commerce and the Pacific Telephone and Telegraph Company. The service was to operate for a year, until June 30, 1929.

The Committee explained that the costs of the demonstration period would be borne principally by the Fund, but that at the conclusion "it is hoped that the system will be taken over by the Federal Government, and that the experience with this plan will serve as a basis for the national development of a weather service especially adapted to the requirements of safe aviation."

Dr. C.-G. Rossby, retained as a technical expert by the Fund, undertook the organization of the weather service; the meteorological work was carried out by members of the staff of the Weather Bureau. After a few months Edward H. Bowie, meteorologist of the Weather Bureau at San Francisco, took charge of the organization.

In July 1929 Mr. Bowie wrote a summary of the operations for publication by the Fund. Entitled "Weather and the Airplane", the Bowie report contained a description of the model meteorological service, and set forth in detail the system of visual ground signals by means of which pilots in flight were informed of conditions ahead.

These signals consisted of canvas strips laid flat on the ground in various combinations of lines and crosses, by means of which pilots were notified of such matters as the height of the cloud ceiling and the amount of cloud in the region just ahead. The signal system, which would be useless in today's high altitude operations, was quite effective in the "contact" flying of that time. The visual weather signals displayed at Bakersfield were particularly helpful to southbound pilots requiring information on weather conditions in the quickly-changing Los Angeles area.

Before takeoff, information on weather conditions and upper-air wind speeds was transmitted to pilots in statistical form. The data were marked up on a large blackboard in conjunction with a series of maps corresponding to varying levels from the surface up to 10,000 feet. A pilot preparing to start a scheduled flight was expected to inform himself on weather conditions by studying these exhibits.

In order to transmit weather data promptly, a system of data transmission was developed with the cooperation of the Pacific Telephone and Telegraph Company, represented on an Air Coordination Committee by Dr. J. C. Hunsaker, then Assistant Vice President of Bell Telephone Laboratories, and later head of the Departments of Mechanical Engineering and Aeronautical Engineering at the Massachusetts Institute of Technology. Dr. Hunsaker, who had become interested in communications in connection with airline operation as early as the spring of 1927, originated the data transmission plan. At first, reports on the weather were transmitted three times a day. Their value to pilots soon proved so great that the frequency was increased to six times a day.

"The model airway in California," said Dr. Hunsaker recently, "was perhaps the most important initiative taken by the Fund. Our whole air transportation system has grown from this experiment, showing that the cooperation of finance, Government, and industry can be effective in advancing the art. For the first time, meteorology, communications, airplanes, and management worked together toward safety and a useful objective."

The model weather service, like the model airline, quickly proved a success. Commercial aviation was by no means the only flying activity to benefit from it. Lieutenant Colonel Gerald Brandt, then in command of the Air Corps Station at Crissy Field, San Francisco, declared that "the Guggenheim experimental airways weather service has done more to raise the morale of the Army Flying Corps than anything else that has happened since I have been associated with it. Formerly, a pilot did not know what was ahead; now he knows, and is prepared."

After a year of operation the government decided to take the airline weather service over, as planned, for continued operation on the West Coast and as a model for such services in other parts of the country.

In its final report on the weather service, the Fund disclosed that the total cost had been remarkably modest: $27,500 for the year. "The expenditure," it said, "is less than the cost of one of the efficient, three-motored monoplanes that have been flying the route for more than a year without accident to plane, pilot or passengers."

7

High on its list of long-range projects, the Fund counted two as of special importance; education and research. It provided for these by establishing schools of aeronautics in leading universities, and making a series of special grants for research.

The first of the Guggenheim schools, The Daniel Guggenheim School of Aeronautics at New York University, had been established before the Fund began operation. Under the direction of its energetic Director, Professor Alexander Klemin, it rapidly became a national center for aeronautics research and education.

It was followed by the Daniel Guggenheim Graduate School of Aeronautics at California Institute of Technology, and its associated Guggenheim Aeronautical Laboratories, set up by a grant of $305,000 from the Fund in 1926. To aid in the development of the School and Laboratories, the Fund invited Dr. Theodore von Kármán, born in Budapest and widely known in Germany for his contributions to the aeronautical sciences, to visit the United States for consultation with Dr. Robert A. Millikan, President of the California Institute of Technology. In addition, Dr. von Kármán was to visit and lecture at other centers of aeronautical education, including Stanford University, Massachusetts Institute of Technology, New York University and the University of Michigan.

Dr. von Kármán arrived toward the end of September, 1926. His visits were enthusiastically received, and the tour was concluded by a series of lectures at the New Museum Building in Washington, D.C. The genius of Dr. von Kármán, who until his death in 1963 was a towering figure in the flight sciences throughout the world, was already apparent on his first visit to the United States. He became a research associate of the California Institute of Technology in 1928, and was named Director of the Guggenheim School of Aeronautics and the Guggenheim Aeronautical Laboratories in 1930, a position he held until 1948. The present Director of the Guggenheim Laboratories is Dr. Clark Millikan, son of Dr. Robert A. Millikan, the late President of California Institute of Technology. Dr. Clark Millikan was closely associated with Dr. von Kármán for many years, and is himself a distinguished contributor to technology in this field.

In 1926 the Fund made a grant of $195,000 to establish The Daniel Guggenheim Aeronautic Laboratory at Stanford University. Conceived from the beginning as a graduate school, the Guggenheim Laboratory grew out of an earlier aeronautical center at Stanford University headed by William F. Durand, later a Guggenheim Medalist. The Guggenheim grant made it possible for this Laboratory to carry on major work in propeller and other aeronautical research.

Later in 1926 the Fund made a grant of $78,000 to the University of Michigan, to establish the Daniel Guggenheim Professorship of Applied Aeronautics and enable the university to complete its aeronautical laboratory.

Early the following year, in January 1927, a grant of $230,000 was made to the Massachusetts Institute of Technology to provide for the construction of the Daniel Guggenheim Aeronautical Laboratory at MIT. A second gift of $34,000 by the Fund, in 1928, made it possible for MIT to establish a graduate course in meteorology and a meteorological research group under the direction of Professor C.-G. Rossby, former Assistant Director of the Weather Bureau.

In 1929 the Fund made a grant of $250,000 to the University of Akron for the establishment of the Daniel Guggenheim Airship Institute at Akron, Ohio. Plans for the Institute were drawn up jointly by the California Institute of Technology and the University of Akron, from a basis of suggestions by the airship industry. A substantial program of research on the aerodynamics, construction and development of lighter-than-air craft was carried on at the Institute.

Two more grants to establish schools of aeronautics in sections of the country which had previously lacked such facilities were made by the Fund in 1930. The first was a gift of $290,000 to the University of Washington. Supplemented by $50,000 appropriated by the Washington State Legislature, it provided for a new building, the Guggenheim Hall of Aeronautics, and the establishment of a curriculum leading to the degree of Bachelor of Science in Aeronautical Engineering.

The second 1930 grant was for $300,000 to the Georgia School of Technology, to establish an aeronautical, engineering and research institute in the South. Construction of the building for this Daniel Guggenheim School of Aeronautics was begun in June 1930; classes were first held in it in January 1931.

Substantial programs of research were promptly begun in all of the Guggenheim schools. Many studies were also carried out under special grants.

Always interested in meteorology, the Fund in July 1929 gave $3,840 to provide an aerologist to the Byrd Antarctic Expedition of that year. It gave $10,000 to Cornell University to enable Dr. William C. Geer to conduct research on the formation of ice on aircraft, resulting in several alternative means of preventing or minimizing ice formation. It gave $8,000, subsequently increased to $17,000, to enable Dr. S. Herbert Anderson, of the University of Washington, to carry on research at Wright Field on the penetration of light through fog.

In May 1927 a research grant of $5,000, subsequently increased to $10,000, was given to help finance the second University of Michigan Greenland Expedition, headed by Professor William H. Hobbs, the principal object of which was to study atmospheric and climatic conditions in Greenland, with special reference to the weather of the north Atlantic.

Other grants included $15,000 to the Harvard University School of Business Administration for a study of the economic and industrial aspects of commercial aviation. The first Research Fellow appointed by Harvard under this grant was Herbert Hoover, Jr.

To establish a center for aerial photographic mapping and surveying, the Fund in June 1929 granted $30,000 to the University of Syracuse, and later made a further grant of $30,000. In the same month a grant was made to Northwestern University School of Law at Chicago, to help establish an Air Law Institute. The total cost of the Institute was $35,000, of which one-third was subscribed by the Fund.

In October 1929 the Fund made a contribution of $140,000 to the Library of Congress, to endow in the Library a Chair of Aeronautics and stimulate the acquisition of aeronautical historical material. The Fund had acquired considerable valuable aeronautical literature, and substantial portions of this was turned over to the Library. Dr. Albert F. Zahm, former Director of the Aerodynamic Laboratory of the United States Navy, was the first appointee to the Library's Chair of Aeronautics.

In 1926 Dr. William F. Durand, one of the trustees of the Fund and Professor Emeritus at Stanford University, recommended the sponsoring of an encyclopedia relating to fundamental aerodynamic theory. The project received the full support of the Fund and a grant of $60,000, and preparation and publication of the work occupied the major part of Dr. Durand's time from 1930 until 1936. The finished encyclopedia comprised six volumes, covering 20 divisions of the field, written by 23 authors. It was published under the title: "Aerodynamic Theory—A General Review of Progress."

8

Liquidation of the Daniel Guggenheim Fund for the Promotion of Aeronautics was completed on February 1, 1930, in Daniel Guggenheim's 74th and last year of life. It had been in operation four years and 15 days.

In his final report Harry Guggenheim wrote: "The Fund feels it has carried out the letter and spirit of its Trusteeship. In the past four years, the public attitude toward aviation has changed from apathetic indifference to enthusiastic support. Not only is there a sound economic basis for aviation so that it is now financially able to take care of itself, but also there have been established in different geographical sections of this country aeronautical engineering and research centers which are second to none in the world.

"With commercial aircraft companies and operators assured of public support and aeronautical science equally assured of continued research, the further development of aviation in this country can best be fulfilled in the typically American manner of private business enterprise. The work of the Fund now passes into other hands."

DR. GODDARD AND HIS ASSISTANTS CHECKING OVER ONE OF HIS ROCKETS
BEFORE FINAL ASSEMBLY IN THE SHOP AT ROSWELL, NEW MEXICO.

It was not, however, the end of Daniel Guggenheim's contributions to the age of flight; in some ways it was only a beginning.

Up in Worcester, Massachusetts, a little-known professor of physics at Clark University was already ushering in a new phase of flight: the vertical dimension which was to culminate in jet propulsion, rockets and missiles, high-altitude research, satellites, and space exploration. He was Dr. Robert H. Goddard, who had begun his studies of rockets in 1909 or earlier, had developed prototypes of the later bazooka and other military solid-propellant rockets during World War I, and had shot the world's first liquid propellant rocket, near Auburn, Massachusetts, on March 16, 1926.

By 1929 Dr. Goddard had carried his rocket development as far as it could be taken under his own resources and with a series of grants from the Smithsonian Institution. On July 17 of that year he shot an instrument-carrying liquid-propellant rocket of some size, and it made noise in proportion, attracting a great deal of unwanted publicity. The incident had at least one happy result: it brought Colonel Lindbergh on a visit to Worcester, and he and Harry called the Worcester physicist's work to the attention of Daniel Guggenheim. With characteristic foresight, Daniel undertook to finance the rocket research for two years at $25,000 a year, and if it met with the approval of a scientific committee headed by Dr. J. C. Merriam, President of the Carnegie Institution of Washington, for two more years after that.

With these Guggenheim grants, continued until the autumn of 1941 by The Daniel and Florence Guggenheim Foundation, Dr. Goddard was able to establish his operations under more favorable conditions at a site near Roswell, New Mexico. There he brought to a high degree of development the basic technology of rocketry and astronautics, and laid the scientific foundations of the space age.

Daniel Guggenheim died at Sands Point near Port Washington, New York, on September 28, 1930. For a time the 162-acre estate and the great house at Sands Point in which he had lived with Mrs. Guggenheim stood empty. In June 1942 Mrs. Guggenheim decided to add further to the Guggenheim benefactions to the flight sciences by deeding the house and estate to the Institute of the Aeronautical Sciences.

It was in this house that the Daniel Guggenheim School of Aeronautics at New York University was born, and here also Daniel Guggenheim first developed his plan for the Daniel Guggenheim Fund for the Promotion of Aeronautics. In offering the estate to the Institute, Mrs. Guggenheim wrote:

"Obviously, I am no specialist in the art or science of aeronautics, but for a score of years aviation has been a familiar subject of discussion in my family life. No cause challenged more keenly the interest of my husband or my son Harry... I know it would delight my husband, were he still living, again to render a service to aviation. Now, in his stead and memory, I have the privilege of making this offer."

During World War II the Navy had urgent need of the buildings and estate for its Special Devices division. For a time it was leased, and in 1951 purchased by the Navy. The purchase price of $332,000 became a part of the permanent funds of the Institute, which merged in 1963 with the American Rocket Society to form the American Institute of Aeronautics and Astronautics. Income from these funds is used to support projects of importance to the advancement of the flight sciences, such as the biennial congress of the International Council of the Aeronautical Sciences, the first of which was held in Madrid, Spain, in 1958.

The "promotion" of the flight sciences which Daniel Guggenheim started in 1925 also continues today in a number of projects sponsored or established by The Daniel and Florence Guggenheim Foundation, of which Harry Guggenheim is President and a Director.* These projects include The Daniel and Florence Guggenheim Jet Propulsion Center at California Institute of Technology, The Daniel and Florence Guggenheim Laboratories for the Aerospace Propulsion Sciences at Princeton University, The Daniel and Florence Guggenheim Institute of Flight Structures at Columbia University, and The Harvard-Guggenheim Center for Aviation Health and Safety, all of which provide for research, advanced education and the dissemination of technical information.

The Daniel and Florence Guggenheim Foundation in 1950 also established still another project which continues a special interest of Daniel Guggenheim: The Daniel and Florence Guggenheim Aviation Safety Center at Cornell University. This center serves as a national "catalytic agent" in the promotion of aviation safety and safety research, working through Government agencies, the armed services, and research institutions both in this country and abroad.

* The other Directors are Mrs. Roger W. Straus, Vice President; Oscar S. Straus II; Robert Guggenheim, Jr.; Joan G. Van de Maele; Albert C. Van de Maele; Roger W. Straus, Jr.; Dana Draper, and George J. Fountaine.

MAIN BUILDING OF THE DANIEL GUGGENHEIM ESTATE AT
SANDS POINT, NEW YORK, GIVEN TO THE INSTITUTE OF THE
AERONAUTICAL SCIENCES (NOW AIAA) BY MRS. GUGGENHEIM.

Harry Guggenheim himself is Chairman of the Foundation Committee of the Center, its governing body; and on this Committee are represented all the principal Government agencies concerned with aviation safety, the armed services, and Cornell University. General E. R. Quesada, former Administrator of the Federal Aviation Agency, is Chairman of the Center's Policy Committee. Its Director is Jerome Lederer, former Director of the Safety Bureau of the Civil Aeronautics Board.

Thus the work undertaken by Daniel Guggenheim more than a generation ago still goes on.

"I am convinced," said General James H. Doolittle recently, "that the clear vision, effective support, and great effort of the Guggenheims, father and son, Daniel and Harry, profoundly influenced the rapid development of safe, efficient commercial and effective military aviation."

And, he might have added, still does profoundly influence them, and much else besides. For the astronaut, riding his capsule around the earth or on voyages to the moon or planets, is no less a product of the forces, ideas, innovations and enthusiasms engendered by the contributions of the Guggenheims than are the millions of airline passengers or the growing international web of airlanes in this still unfolding, still developing Age of Flight.

Sources:
Files of the Daniel Guggenheim Fund for the Promotion of Aeronautics, Library of Congress; files of the Daniel and Florence Guggenheim Foundation, 120 Broadway, New York; material in the Library of the American Institute of Aeronautics and Astronautics and the Engineering Societies' Library; correspondence and interviews with Harry F. Guggenheim, General James H. Doolittle, General Charles A. Lindbergh, Dr. Theodore P. Wright, Dr. J. C. Hunsaker, and others; *America Fledges Wings*, by Reginald M. Cleveland (Pitman, New York, 1942); *Pioneering in Aeronautics*, edited by Reginald M. Cleveland (Guggenheim Medal Board of Award, 1952); 1961 *Report of the President*, The Daniel and Florence Guggenheim Foundation; *The Coming Age of Rocket Power*, by G. Edward Pendray (Harper & Row, New York, 1945, 1947); *Seed Money: The Guggenheim Story*, by Milton Lomask (Farrar, Straus & Company, New York, 1964).

THE
DANIEL GUGGENHEIM
MEDAL

The Daniel Guggenheim Medal, awarded "for great achievement in aeronautics," was established by the Fund in 1927 with an initial grant of $15,000. The purpose was to honor those who had made significant contributions to the advancement of flight and thus to encourage others to aspire to similar achievement.

Since at that time there was no single technical society representing aeronautics, a non-profit corporation known as The Daniel Guggenheim Medal Fund, Inc. was established to receive and administer the grant. Half of the directors were named by the American Society of Mechanical Engineers and half by the Society of Automotive Engineers. The original Board of Award consisted of the eight directors of the Fund, and one member each designated by leading technical organizations in seven foreign countries: Canada, England, France, Germany, Holland, Italy and Japan.

The first award, for the year 1929, was made on May 1 of that year, the Board of Award consisting of Dr. William F. Durand, E. T. Jones, Elmer A. Sperry, Jr., Arthur Nutt, Howard E. Coffin, Paul G. Zimmerman, E. E. Aldrin and Edward P. Warner, also Griffith Brewer of England, A. Rateau of France, Johann Schuette of Germany, Guilo Costanzi of Italy, and Baron Chuzaburo Shiba of Japan.

The Board decided unanimously to award the first Guggenheim Medal to Orville Wright, and Mr. Wright received it in Washington, D.C. in April 1930, at ceremonies which were part of the 50th anniversary celebration of the founding of the American Society of Mechanical Engineers.

The medal has been awarded each year since 1929. To date a total of 35 persons who have made signal contributions to the age of flight have been honored in this way.

The Daniel Guggenheim Medal Fund, Inc. continued to operate as an entity for ten years. In this period it became evident that management of a separate corporation could be a considerable burden on the time of the directors. Accordingly, on August 15, 1938, a special meeting voted to dissolve the corporation and vest the management of the Medal fund in the United Engineering Trustees, Inc. The former board of directors, plus all living American recipients of the Medal, was re-established as The Daniel Guggenheim Medal Board of Award, a committee of United Engineering Trustees, Inc.

At present the Board of Award consist of 14 Life Members (American recipients of the Medal), three representatives each of the American Society of Mechanical Engineers, the Society of Automotive Engineers, and the American Institute of Aeronautics and Astronautics, and eight international members, a total of 31. Dr. Ernest Kirkendall, Secretary and General Manager of United Engineering Trustees, Inc., serves as Secretary to the Medal Board of Award. The Board meets annually to select a new recipient, and the Medal is usually presented, in rotation, at the annual meetings of the three technical societies represented on the Board of Award.

THE
GUGGENHEIM MEDALISTS
1929-1963

BIOGRAPHICAL
SKETCHES

For the design and construction, with his brother now deceased, of the first successful engine-propelled airplane.

ORVILLE WRIGHT

The age of manned flight in heavier-than-air craft began on December 17, 1903, when Orville Wright, born August 19, 1871, at Dayton, Ohio, and his brother Wilbur (1867–1912) flew a propeller-driven airplane near Kitty Hawk, North Carolina.

Interested by Lilienthal's gliding experiments in Germany, the Wrights about 1896 began to study the available literature on flight, and concluded that the outstanding problem was equilibrium. By 1899 they had conceived the idea of warping the wings to produce a differential in lift at the opposing tips (aileron control) and tested the principle successfully with a large biplane kite. In 1900 and 1901, on the dunes near Kitty Hawk, they flew man-carrying gliders similar in form to Chanute's biplane and with wing curvatures adapted from Lilienthal and others, but found the lift much below expectation.

Convinced that existing data were unreliable, they then measured the characteristics of some 200 model airfoils, employing a small wind tunnel and balances of their own design. From these new data, a third glider was constructed and successfully tested in 1902. To this machine they also added a vertical rudder, rigged to operate cooperatively with the wing-tip controls. By October 1902 the Wrights had thus achieved an airplane controllable about all three axes at the will of the pilot.

The brothers now undertook the development of a suitable power plant, and within a year produced a satisfactory 4-cylinder 16-horsepower engine and remarkably efficient propellers, designed from their wind tunnel data on airfoils. It was with this powerplant, installed in a larger version of the 1902 glider, that the first powered flights in history were accomplished in 1903. Improvements were tested in new powered airplanes in more than 150 flights near Dayton in 1904–05.

Believing the first use of the now practical airplane would be in war, the Wrights offered their patent and scientific data to the U.S. War Department, which rejected their overtures. Rebuffed at home, they sought a market in Europe. At last, in 1908, purchase offers were received from a French syndicate and the U.S. Government, and demonstration trials took place concurrently in the two countries. Orville made the famous Army acceptance tests at Ft. Myer, Virginia; Wilbur flew in France.

Under the strain of bitter litigation in defense of their pioneer patent, Wilbur Wright died suddenly in 1912. In 1915 Orville sold the Wright Company and, after service as a consulting engineer in World War I, confined his public aviation activities to membership in the National Advisory Committee for Aeronautics. He also took a leading part in developing the automatic stabilizer and pilotless aircraft and held a patent on the split wing-flap. He died on January 30, 1948, the only man ever to see a U.S. national monument—the Wright Brothers Memorial at Kill Devil Hill—erected in his honor during his lifetime.

For pioneer and creative work in the theory of dynamics.

LUDWIG PRANDTL

Every successful mechanical art must rest soundly upon knowledge of nature, and it was Ludwig Prandtl who first demonstrated in a substantial way the importance of scientific research to human flight. He was the creator of modern concepts of wing theory, boundary layer mechanics, and turbulence, and was thus one of the principal progenitors of the science of aerodynamics.

Prandtl was born February 4, 1875, at Freising, Bavaria. He studied mechanical engineering at the Munich Technical High School, and in 1900 was granted the degree of Doctor of Philosophy from the University of Munich. In the same year he entered the Nuremberg works of the Maschinenfabrik Augsburg-Nürnberg as an engineer, his first assignment being to redesign an installation for removing shavings by suction. By studying the aerodynamical principles involved, he was able to improve the equipment to such an extent that the company thereafter introduced it as a new product.

In the fall of 1901 Prandtl became Professor of Mechanics in the Hanover Technical High School, where he continued his research on the laws of air currents, particularly the behavior of the boundary layers of fluid as affected by wall friction. In 1904 he moved to the University of Göttingen, where he accepted the direction of the Institute for Technical Physics.

Two years later, in 1906, the Motorluftschiff-Studien-Gesellschaft was formed to develop the Parsifal airship. Prandtl, while continuing his university work, was chosen a member of the engineering committee of the company. In this capacity he suggested the construction of a wind tunnel, which was put into operation in 1909.

Beginning in 1910 Prandtl occupied himself with research on the aerodynamic behavior of airplane wings, and found laws showing the dependence of lift on the angle of attack and the aspect ratio. The first World War further stimulated his scientific work. With the aid of the German military establishment, a new and considerably larger wind tunnel was built, which long supplied the chief data for the aerodynamic calculations of the German aviation industry.

In 1937 he became President of the Board of Directors of the Aerodynamic Research Laboratory at Göttingen, where most of his later researches were conducted. Among the important subjects treated by him were the theory of frictional layers, the wing theory, contributions to the understanding of flow in compressible fluids and the motions of gases, the theory of plastic deformation, and the theory of turbulent flow of fluids.

Prandtl visited the United States in 1929, when an invitation to participate in the World Engineering Congress in Tokyo gave him an opportunity for a trip around the world. He died at Göttingen, Germany, on August 15, 1953.

FREDERICK WILLIAM LANCHESTER

Probably the most eminent British mechanical engineer of his generation, Frederick William Lanchester's life work was the motor car: its engine, transmission, suspension and stability. Despite this, he was able to make at least two contributions to the science and engineering of aircraft which established him as a major architect of the age of flight as well.

Born at Lewisham, England, on October 23, 1868, Lanchester's education was somewhat irregular. He first studied at the Royal College of Science, South Kensington, England, and later read for engineering in the South Kensington Library, attending engineering lectures at the Finsbury Technical College in the evenings.

From 1889 to 1892 he was designer and Assistant Works Manager of the Forward Gas Engine Company, specializing in internal combustion engines. From 1892 to 1895 he was engaged in developmental work on high speed motors and experimental work in aerodynamics. The development of petrol motors, motor launches and the Lanchester car occupied his energies from 1894 until 1899.

In the latter year the Lanchester Motor Company, Ltd. was formed, and he served as General Manager and Chief Engineer until 1904. He thereafter continued as consulting engineer until 1914; meantime also serving as consulting engineer and technical advisor to other engine and automobile companies.

Among his numerous successful inventions relating to the internal combustion engine were the gas engine starter, developed in 1890; the balanced reciprocating engine and the surface carburetor in 1895, an improved process for manufacturing piston rings in 1909, the torsional crankshaft damper in 1910, and the harmonic balancer in 1911.

Aeronautical science to Lanchester was always a spare-time recreation. One of his earliest contributions was an analysis of the dynamical stability of airplane flight, made in 1897, some years before there were any airplanes. So penetrating was the insight shown that this analysis served as the inspiration and foundation for the later work of Bryan, Bairstow, Hunsaker and many others, who were able to apply Lanchester's precepts while using modern wind tunnels.

He was also the first to propound the vortex theory of flight and its engineering application to the design of airplanes, which was followed up later by Prandtl and others. The vortex theory was the basis of a paper read by Lanchester before the Birmingham National History and Philosophical Society in 1894, and a further paper submitted to the Physical Society of London in 1897.

Lanchester was one of the original members of the Aeronautical Research Committee under the chairmanship of Lord Rayleigh. In 1926 he gave the Wilbur Wright Memorial Lecture on the subject: "Sustentation in Flight." He died March 8, 1946, at the age of 77.

MEDALIST FOR 1932

*For development of the theory and
practice of the Autogiro.*

JUAN DE LA CIERVA

A man of questing mind who dared to follow new and stimulating ideas was Juan de la Cierva y Codorniu, born September 21, 1895, at Murcia, Spain, educated in Murcia and Madrid, and graduated in 1919 from the Special Technical College in Madrid as an Ingeniero de Caminos, Canales y Puertos (civil engineer). His ambition had been to become an aeronautical engineer, but no technical school in Spain offered that branch of engineering.

In 1910, at the age of 15, he built two gliders with the help of some friends. The following year he built a mechanically-propelled airplane which flew unexpectedly well and was probably the first Spanish-built plane to take the air.

In 1918 the Spanish Government opened an aircraft competition to provide fighters, reconnaissance and bombing machines for military use. There were many competitors for the first two types, so Cierva decided to build a bomber. Backed financially by his father and a friend, he developed a biplane powered with two Hispano-Suiza engines of 225 horsepower each. The plane had a capacity for carrying more than a ton of bombs or 14 passengers and two pilots, and incorporated new and original features, including an airfoil section developed by purely mathematical methods which Cierva himself devised. This promising machine crashed while being tested in May 1919, and was completely destroyed.

Convinced by this experience that the limitations of fixed-wing aircraft were too great to overcome, Cierva turned to the study of flying machines in which the wings would have motion relative to the body of the craft; more especially, those in which motion of the wings could be independent of any power applied directly to them. Thus the principle of the Autogiro was born.

Cierva started developing Autogiros early in 1920. But not until January 1923, after the solution of a number of difficult technical problems, did he succeed in producing a craft capable of sustained flight. A series of straight-line flights was made at the Getafe Aerodrome near Madrid on the 17th of that month. On the 31st, at Cuatro Vientos Aerodrome, a complete circuit of approximately 4 kilometers was successfully flown at an altitude of more than 25 meters. In 1923 and 1925, two more machines were built and tested. By 1925 Cierva had produced an Autogiro capable of showing fully the possibilities of the system. In 1928 he was the first person to fly across the English Channel by Autogiro.

There followed a period during which he worked energetically with manufacturing companies in England, the United States, France, and Germany in producing and promoting Autogiros. Among these companies was the Autogiro Company of America, of which he was a director. Financial as well as technical success seemed almost within his grasp when he was killed in an air transport crash at Croydon Airport, England, on December 9, 1936.

MEDALIST FOR 1933

For contributions to the science of aerodynamics, to the science and art of aircraft design, and to the practical construction and utilization of rigid airships.

JEROME CLARKE HUNSAKER

The contributions of Jerome Clarke Hunsaker to the development of flight and the flight sciences are so many and varied as almost to defy classification. He was born August 26, 1886, at Creston, Iowa; educated in the public schools of Detroit and Saginaw, Michigan; at the United States Naval Academy, from which he was graduated in 1908 at the head of his class, and at Massachusetts Institute of Technology.

Hunsaker was early interested in aeronautics, but airplane design as an engineering art did not then exist in this country. With the aid of Mrs. Hunsaker, the former Alice Avery, he translated Eiffel's pioneer work on wind tunnel testing of airplane models, and in 1913 went to Paris to join Eiffel's assistants. Returning the following year, he inaugurated wind tunnel research at MIT to determine the aerodynamical data necessary for rational aircraft design. This work formed the basis in October 1914 for a graduate course in aeronautical engineering at MIT, the first in the United

States. In 1916 MIT awarded him the degree of Doctor of Science for wind tunnel research on dynamical stability.

In 1916 he was put in charge of the Aircraft Division of the Navy Bureau of Construction and Repair, and soon was responsible for the design, construction and procurement of all Naval aircraft. In 1918 he was charged with two special engineering projects: to build a Zeppelin, and to design and build a flying boat to cross the Atlantic. The flying boat project became known as the "NC" (Navy Curtiss) and four units were built. Three started from Newfoundland in May 1919; two were wrecked near the Azores, but the NC-4 under Commander A. C. Reed continued on to Lisbon and Plymouth, the first crossing of the Atlantic by aircraft of any type. The Zeppelin project resulted in completion of the airship *Shenandoah*, the first Zeppelin-type ship to employ helium as the lifting gas.

In 1921 Hunsaker was transferred to the newly organized Navy Bureau of Aeronautics, and here had an opportunity to realize practical results from the great accumulation of research and experimental data obtained during the war. In 1923 he was detailed as Assistant Naval Attaché at London, Paris, the Hague, Rome and Berlin, remaining on this duty until 1926, when he resigned to join the research staff of the Bell Telephone Laboratories in New York, as Assistant Vice President. He there developed wire and radio communication services for civil aviation, beginning with a system organized for the Daniel Guggenheim Fund for the Promotion of Aeronautics.

In 1928 he became a Vice President of the Goodyear-Zeppelin Corporation, which had been formed to build the *Akron* and *Macon* for the Navy. Following completion of these airships he returned to MIT as head of the Departments of Mechanical Engineering and Aeronautical Engineering. In 1941 he was elected Chairman of the National Advisory Committee for Aeronautics, and was reelected annually for sixteen years.

MEDALIST FOR 1934

For successful pioneering and achievement in aircraft manufacturing and air transport.

WILLIAM EDWARD BOEING

As one of the world's foremost aircraft manufacturers, William Edward Boeing brought to the airplane industry, when it was most needed, industrial leadership backed by ample resources. He thus helped to change into a great industry what had previously been little more than a venturous sport.

Born October 1, 1881, in Detroit, Michigan, and educated in the United States and Switzerland, Boeing entered the Sheffield Scientific School at Yale University, but dropped out in 1903, a year short of a diploma, to move to Grays Harbor, Washington, where he bought extensive timberlands.

In 1914, after making several airplane flights, Boeing and a friend, Conrad Westervelt, decided to build their own plane. With typical thoroughness, Boeing first went to Los Angeles, in 1915, and took flying instruction from Glenn L. Martin. He purchased a Martin seaplane and became a proficient pilot. Only then did he put a crew to work designing and building the first two Boeing aircraft, the B & W float-planes, in a hangar on the shore of Lake Union in Seattle.

Encouraged by the success of these planes, which flew in 1916, he incorporated the Pacific Aero Products Company, which soon became the Boeing Airplane Company. The new company, occupying a small converted shipyard on the Duwamish River in Seattle, grew to be one of the largest aircraft plants in the world, pioneering new designs and ideas. Boeing military and commercial planes—the B-17, B-29, B-47 and B-52 bombers; the Stratoliners, Stratocruisers, and the 707, 720, and 727 jet transports—have become world famous.

One of the earliest airplanes produced by the company, the B-1 Flying Boat, was purchased in 1920 by Edward Hubbard for use on the first regular air mail run between Seattle and Victoria, B.C. In 1919 Hubbard and Boeing had carried the first sack of mail flown to the United States from Canada, in a Boeing Model C float-plane.

In 1927 Boeing branched into the field of air transportation. In a joint bid with Edward Hubbard, the Boeing company won a U.S. Government contract to operate an air mail route from San Francisco to Chicago. When it began operation, on July 1, 1927, this air mail line of 1,950 miles was the longest in the world operated by one interest.

Boeing Air Transport early led the field in developing and proving advanced ideas of passenger airline operation. Its planes were the first to fly passengers at night on regular schedules over long distances, to have two pilots and a stewardess, and to use constant contact between pilot and ground by two-way radio telephone.

Boeing retired from the industry in 1934 shortly after his airline was separated, as United Air Lines, from the parent company. He died on September 28, 1956, while on his yacht on Puget Sound.

For notable achievement as pioneer in laboratory research and theory of aeronautics; distinguished contributions to the theory and development of aircraft propellers.

WILLIAM FREDERICK DURAND

As teacher, researcher, theorist, administrator and innovator, William Frederick Durand devoted a long and active life to the development and improvement of aircraft, to aeronautical theory, and to the training of men who were destined to carry on his work and apply it in practice.

Born at Beacon Falls, Connecticut, on March 5, 1859, he was educated at Derby, Connecticut, and at the United States Naval Academy, where he was graduated with honors in 1880.

Remaining in the Naval Service until 1887, he resigned to take up teaching as a life profession. Appointed first as Professor of Mechanical Engineering at Michigan State College, he transferred to Cornell University in 1891, there taking charge of the newly-organized graduate school of Marine Engineering and Naval Architecture. In 1904 he took the chair of Mechanical Engineering at Stanford

University, remaining until 1924 when, by age limit, he was retired as Professor Emeritus. Retirement, however, did not end Durand's useful career; he continued to be occupied with numerous important engineering and scientific undertakings.

Problems in fluid mechanics early attracted his attention. His first published technical article, written while he was attached to the U.S.S. *Tennessee,* was concerned with ship propulsion. This was followed in later years by extended experimental research and a long series of papers dealing with the general problem of the screw propeller, both for ship propulsion and aircraft.

When, in 1914, a move was made toward the establishment of a National Advisory Committee for Aeronautics, Durand was invited to Washington to join the undertaking. The Committee was officially formed the following year, and he was appointed a member by President Wilson. He was elected Chairman of the Committee in 1916. Under his direction a service of examination and advice regarding aeronautic patents was organized in the NACA. Another undertaking was the development of plans for the NACA's laboratory at Langley Field and the preparation of designs for the first NACA windtunnel.

Following his retirement from Stanford, he served for a year as President of the American Society of Mechanical Engineers. In 1925 he was invited to become a trustee of the Daniel Guggenheim Fund for the Promotion of Aeronautics, and continued in this capacity during the active life of the Fund, from 1925 until 1930. Among the Fund-sponsored projects he undertook was the preparation, as general editor, of an encyclopedia of fundamental aerodynamic theory written as a series of monographs by recognized authorities. The monographs, twenty in number, were published in six volumes, totalling 2,000 pages of text.

Honored the world over for his technical contributions, Durand died in Brooklyn, New York, August 10, 1958, at the age of 99.

For pioneer and creative work in the theory of dynamics.

GEORGE WILLIAM LEWIS

George William Lewis was one of the great American leaders of aeronautical research. Under his direction, as chief executive of the National Advisory Committee for Aeronautics (NACA), the age of flight took great forward strides, solidly grounded in science and technology.

He was born at Ithaca, New York, on March 10, 1882; received the degree of M.E. from Cornell University in 1908, and the degree of M.M.E. in 1910. He was a member of the Swarthmore College faculty from 1910 until 1917, then became Engineer-in-charge at Clarke-Thomson Research, Philadelphia, where he remained until 1919. He joined NACA as Executive Officer in 1919, and became its Director of Aeronautical Research in 1924, from which position he resigned because of health on September 1, 1947. He remained in NACA service as Research Consultant until his death on July 12, 1948.

In 1919 the NACA staff totaled 43, including the pioneer research staff of NACA's Langley Laboratory, located at Langley Field, Virginia. Lewis recruited and inspired young scientists, engineers, and mathematicians, and welded them into effective, balanced research teams. He pioneered novel methods of flight research, new ideas for recording instruments, and new methods and facilities for research on engines, propellers, structures, seaplanes, ice prevention, helicopters, and many other branches of aerodynamics. He developed and made use of many wind tunnels, including variable-density, full-scale, refrigerated, free-flight, gust, transonic, and supersonic types.

By 1938 Hitler had multiplied German air research facilities until they were five times the magnitude of those available in the United States. This challenge to American leadership was clearly presented to the President and the Congress by Lewis, who arranged to spend May 1939 in Germany, touring the new air research facilities. In June he testified before Congress in detail, and reported the opinion of numerous German scientists and professors, that war would start before the next snow fell.

Congress approved the doubling of NACA's facilities and staff at Langley, and the construction of a second major NACA station, now known as the Ames Research Center, at Moffett Field, California. A year later, Congress authorized the NACA Aircraft Engine Research Laboratory at Cleveland, Ohio, now known as Lewis Research Center in honor of Dr. Lewis.

NACA research facilities built during Lewis' regime cost about $80,000,000 and, although often new in concept and design, never failed to meet their planned performance. When failing health caused him to resign as Director of Aeronautical Research in 1947, the seventeen members of NACA signed a testimonial praising Lewis for "inspiring leadership", and declared: "The Committee's research organization has won the confidence and respect... of the aeronautical world, and made scientific and technical contributions of inestimable value to the national security."

*For notable contributions to trans-
oceanic air transport and to international cooperation in aeronautics.*

HUGO ECKENER

Hugo Eckener, born on August 10, 1868, at Flensburg, Schleswig-Holstein, was destined to become the world's greatest authority on lighter-than-air ships and their navigation.

Starting life as a journalist, he wrote in 1904 a series of scoffing and critical articles for the *Frankfurter Zeitung* about Count Ferdinand von Zeppelin, who was then experimenting with lighter-than-air craft. Count Zeppelin, meeting him at a yachting party, adroitly drew his young critic into a frank discussion of airship problems. Eckener soon afterward entered the service of the Luftschiffbau Zeppelin, Zeppelin's airship company.

When the first World War began, Eckener was assigned to train dirigible commanders for the German Navy. Following the war he organized air transportation in Germany with the airships *Bodensee* and *Nordstern*, and maintained the service until these ships were delivered to the Allies as part of the war reparations. In 1922 he became General Manager of the Zeppelin Company, and two years later piloted the reparations airship *ZR-3* across the Atlantic from Friedrichshafen to Lakehurst, New Jersey, where it was delivered to the United States Navy, and later rechristened the *Los Angeles.*

In 1928 he commanded the *Graf Zeppelin* on the first commercial trans-Atlantic flight. This great Zeppelin, the 117th in a dynasty of airships built in Germany, made the 6,168-mile westward voyage with 20 passengers and a crew of 40 in 111 hours, 44 minutes. In 1929 Eckener commanded the *Graf Zeppelin* on a round-the-world flight from Friedrichshafen back to Friedrichshafen with a crew of 41 and 20 passengers, making the 21,255-mile voyage in 20 days, four hours and 14 minutes elapsed time, of which 300 hours and 20 minutes were flight time.

By May 1937 the *Graf Zeppelin* had made 590 flights, cruised 1,053,381 miles, and had carried 13,110 passengers and 235,300 pounds of mail and freight, mainly in service between Germany and Brazil. In 1936 Eckener inaugurated trans-Atlantic commercial passenger and mail service with the giant new dirigible *Hindenburg*, acting as pilot on her first voyage. During 1936 and one month in 1937 the *Hindenburg* made ten round trips between Frankfurt and Lakehurst, and eight to Rio de Janeiro, carrying 3,059 passengers and 41,000 pounds of mail and freight. Fire of undetermined origin destroyed the hydrogen-filled airship in one of the world's most spectacular disasters as she was coming in for a landing at Lakehurst on her first voyage of the 1937 season.

Following the loss of the *Hindenburg*, Eckener strove in vain to obtain from the United States a supply of helium for the *Hindenburg's* successor, the *H2-130*, also named *Graf Zeppelin*. Zeppelin plants during World War II were diverted to other purposes, and airship activities in Germany were not resumed. Eckener came to the United States for a short time in 1947 to aid the experts of the Goodyear Aircraft Corporation. He died at Friedrichshafen on August 14, 1954.

For contributions to the development of aircraft engine design and for the specific design of the sleeve-valve aircraft engine.

SIR ROY FEDDEN

The advancement of aeronautics in the 20's and 30's was a triumph of mingled daring, skill, science, engineering, construction; and not least, the rapid development of better, more powerful, more reliable engines.

To the latter art one of the principal contributors was Alfred Hubert Roy Fedden, born in Bristol, England, on June 6, 1885; in his time to become one of the world's leading authorities on aircraft power plants. He was knighted in 1942 for his contributions to aeronautics.

Fedden was educated at Clifton College, and took the engineering course at Bristol Merchant Venturers Technical College. In 1906, at the age of 21, he joined Brazil Straker and Company, Fishponds, Bristol, and for two years was in charge of touring car design. From 1909 to 1914 he was Chief Engineer; in 1914 he became Director and was in charge of engineering on internal combustion engines.

In the period from 1915 until the end of World War I he was engaged in aircraft engine manufacture, producing the Rolls-Royce, Hawke and Falcon liquid-cooled engines and the 8-cylinder Renault air-cooled engine. In 1920 the Bristol Aeroplane Company appointed him Chief Engineer of its Engine Department, a position he held until 1942. Here he completed development of the Jupiter engine, which earned world-wide recognition for reliability and efficiency. With restless eagerness for improvement, he continued to develop new and successful air-cooled engines, including the Lucifer, Mercury, Cherub and Pegasus.

While these poppet-valve engines were in course of development and refinement, he also carried out intensive research on single sleeve-valve engines, for Fedden was a firm believer in the advantages of this design. The earliest 9-cylinder sleeve-valve radial air-cooled aircraft engine was the Perseus, built in 1932, the first sleeve-valve engine to be used for aircraft propulsion. The Perseus was followed by a series of notable sleeve-valve engines, including the Aquila, Tarus, Hercules and Centaurus.

During World War II Fedden served as special advisor to the Ministry of Aircraft Production, and after the war as aircraft advisor to NATO. He remained active as a consultant until 1960.

Continually alert to coming developments, Fedden early perceived the possibilities of jet propulsion in commercial as well as military aviation. He was responsible for the original layout of the Bristol Theseus gas turbine. In delivering the 32nd Wilbur Wright Memorial Lecture before the Royal Aeronautical Society in 1944, he urged development of the turbine to increase flexibility and reduce fuel consumption, forecasting that "for high speed civilian flying at high altitudes, pure jet propulsion could compete with reciprocating engines for periods in excess of three hours and ranges over 1500 miles."

For outstanding contributions to the design and construction of transport airplanes.

DONALD WILLS DOUGLAS

The name of Donald Wills Douglas has become synonymous with the massive transport of men and goods through the air at ever-increasing speeds, and the beginnings of the age of space exploration.

Born in Brooklyn, New York, on April 6, 1892, he entered the United States Naval Academy in 1909, and in that year saw Orville Wright demonstrate the Wright flying machine to the United States Army at Ft. Myer, Virginia. Better to follow his growing interest in aviation, he resigned after three years at the Academy to enter the Massachusetts Institute of Technology, where he was graduated in 1914.

From mid-1914 to mid-1915 he was assistant to Dr. Jerome C. Hunsaker at MIT, in the graduate course in aerodynamics. A few months later he joined the Glenn L. Martin Company as Chief Engineer. In the following year he went to Washington as Chief Civilian Engineer of the United States Signal Corps.

76

In 1920 he moved his family to California to start his own airplane manufacturing venture. Not yet 30, his assets totalled $600. His first contract was to build an airplane for a Los Angeles sportsmen who wanted to cross the North American continent non-stop by air. With six former associates at the Martin Company, he produced a two-place wood and fabric biplane called the *Cloudster*. It was the first U.S. airplane ever to get off the ground with a useful load equal to its own weight.

World recognition first came to Douglas in 1924, when U.S. Army pilots, flying Douglas World Cruisers, made an historic round-the-world flight covering 27,553 miles in 15 days, 11 hours and seven minutes of flying time. In 1935 Douglas developed the famous DC-3, a twin-engine airliner that became the most widely-used in the world. The basic DC-3 design was adapted during World War II to the C-47 military transport, used in every theatre of war and by all Allied powers.

Next came the B-19 bomber, until 1948 the largest land-based aircraft ever built. The B-19 paved the way for the new generation of super-bombers of World War II. A notable series of airliners and military transports followed, including the DC-4, the C-54, the DC-6, and the DC-7. Douglas' DC-8 jet transport first went into airline service September 18, 1959.

The company has also produced guided missiles for the Army, Navy and Air Force since 1940. In the large rocket field it had airframe development responsibility for Thor, the Air Force intermediate-range ballistic missile.

During World War II Douglas served as President of the National Aircraft War Production Council, and subsequently was President of its successor, the Aircraft Industry Association. For his outstanding contributions to the Allied victory he was awarded the Certificate of Merit by President Truman.

MEDALIST FOR 1940

For contributions to aeronautical development and the production of many types of aircraft of high performance.

GLENN LUTHER MARTIN

As a young man in his late 'teens Glenn Luther Martin read in the newspapers of the Wright brothers' flight at Kitty Hawk, and knew with complete conviction that he too would someday build airplanes and fly them.

Born in Macksburg, Iowa, on January 17, 1886, he received his education at Kansas Wesleyan University in Salina. His family moved to Santa Ana, California, in 1905, and there he began his aeronautical career by building a biplane glider in which, with characteristic thoroughness, he practiced flying privately until he was sure he had mastered it. He then rented an abandoned church, and began construction of his first powered biplane.

When the new craft was ready, two years later, he taxied for days to get the feel of it. He made his first powered flight on August 1, 1909, covering 100 feet at a two-foot altitude. For several weeks he continued low flights, following each hop with a period of study and adjustment.

78

His first advertised exhibition flight took place in November 1910, after which the plane was put on exhibition, raising several hundred dollars which young Martin used toward the construction of his second plane. During 1911 he barnstormed all over the West. World-wide attention was focussed on him when, on May 10, 1912, he flew a Martin-built seaplane from Newport Bay, near Los Angeles, to Catalina Island and back, a distance of 38 miles.

While continuing his public appearances, which involved a great variety of feats and "firsts", he moved his factory to Los Angeles and started a flying school. In 1913 he produced a four-passenger seaplane, and using a simple cross-hair bomb-sight, made one of the earliest aircraft bombing tests. He invented the first free-fall parachute, and among the top sensations of 1913 were parachute jumps made by Miss Tiny Broadwick from airplanes piloted by Martin.

In January 1918 he went to Washington with plans for a new bomber, and received an order to build several models. The first rolled out of his new plant, in Cleveland, Ohio, only six months later: the MB-1, a twin-engined biplane capable of carrying a bomb load of 1,500 pounds. In a few years Martin aircraft were in such demand that the plant in Cleveland was no longer adequate, and in 1929 he moved the business to Middle River, twelve miles from Baltimore. Here he began to turn out peacetime aircraft such as the China Clipper, used in the Pacific by Pan American Airways, and warplanes such as the B-10 twin-engine bomber, which won the Collier Trophy for 1932.

In World War II the plant at Middle River produced such warplanes as the B-26 Marauder and the Martin Mars, as well as PBM Mariners. After the war, the company continued to develop transport aircraft, jet bombers and long-range flying boats, and to this series added rockets and guided missiles. Glenn Martin retired from active direction of the company in 1952, and died in Baltimore on December 4, 1955.

MEDALIST FOR 1941

*For the development and successful
operation of oceanic air transport.*

JUAN TERRY TRIPPE

It has been said that the sun never sets on the wings of Pan American Clippers—a statement celebrating both the worldwide character of Pan American Airways and the almost legendary skill in management and business diplomacy of Juan Terry Trippe, its chief executive.

Born at Seabright, New Jersey, on June 27, 1899, Trippe entered Yale University in the fall of 1917. In December of the same year he joined the Navy, qualifying as a night bomber pilot, receiving an ensign's commission. Returning to Yale, he was graduated with the class of 1922.

After a year in banking he entered commercial aviation, and in 1923 organized Long Island Airways which, with seven war-vintage planes, carried out sightseeing flights, furnished charter service, and did contract work for motion picture concerns.

When the United States Post Office Department offered air mail contracts to private companies, Trippe and a group of friends organized Colonial Air Transport, Inc. which received the first U.S. air mail contract, Trippe serving as chief executive and managing director. He soon proposed to expand Colonial's services, and when the stockholders opposed the move, Trippe resigned. A few months later he founded Pan American Airways, which began operations with a 90-mile route from Florida to Cuba. Soon Pan American was flying to the Caribbean and South America. Mail and passenger service across the Pacific and Atlantic, and in Alaska, followed. The first scheduled round-the-world air service was inaugurated in 1947. On July 2, 1962, Pan American made its 100,000th trans-Atlantic crossing.

Mass transportation at fares the average man could afford had long been a goal of Trippe's. In 1948 Pan American began low-cost, tourist-class services to Latin America, and finally in 1952 won the adoption of this low-fare tourist service for general use. In 1957 Pan American again pioneered a still lower fare—the economy class. In July 1963 Mr. Trippe announced that his company would sponsor a trans-Atlantic fare of only $160, a 39 per cent reduction.

On October 13, 1955, Trippe took the first step into the Jet Age by placing an order for 45 American-built commercial jet transports—the first such order signed by a United States airline. Jet passenger service began on October 26, 1958, when the first U.S. commercial trans-Atlantic jet flight took off from New York for Paris. Pan American jets soon were linking 100 cities in all parts of the globe. Mr. Trippe also led the way into the Supersonic Age by ordering six supersonic transports in the summer of 1963.

Mr. Trippe holds many positions in civic and charitable associations. He has been decorated by the U.S. and numerous foreign governments and awarded honorary degrees from seven universities. Among his awards and decorations are the Collier Trophy, the Harmon Aviation Trophy and the U.S. Medal for Merit.

MEDALIST FOR 1942

For notable achievements in the advancements of both the art and the science of aeronautics.

JAMES HAROLD DOOLITTLE

The age of flight has produced many remarkable men, but few so protean in abilities and accomplishment as James Harold Doolittle.

Born in Alameda, California, on December 14, 1896, he lived in Alaska until he was eleven. Enlisting in the United States Army Signal Corps in World War I, he quickly won his wings and was commissioned a Second Lieutenant. He left college in his senior year, in 1917, to enlist, and the University of California conferred the degree of Bachelor of Arts on him in 1923. In September of the same year he flew from Pablo Beach, Florida, to San Diego, California, with one stop, becoming the first man to fly across the United States in less than 24 hours.

He was graduated from Massachusetts Institute of Technology in 1924 with the degree of Master of Science, and in 1925 with the degree of Doctor of Science in aeronautical engineering. In October of that year he won the Schneider Trophy Race.

82

In April 1926 he went to South America on airplane demonstration flights. In an accident in Chile, unconnected with flying, he broke both ankles. Not to be balked in his effort to fly the American military airplane he was demonstrating, he put his plane through its paces with his ankles in casts and his feet fastened to the controls.

In September 1927 he was sent to Mitchel Field, at the request of the Daniel Guggenheim Fund for the Promotion of Aeronautics, to assist in fog flying experiments. During this assignment, flight instruments now in universal use were developed, and Doolittle, in a hooded cockpit, accomplished the first flight ever made completely on instruments.

In 1930 he became manager of the Aviation Department of the Shell Oil Company. In 1940 he was recalled to active duty. Promoted in 1942 to Lieutenant Colonel, he was assigned to Headquarters, Army Air Force, in Washington, whereupon he organized and carried out one of the most daring and extraordinary operations of World War II, leading a squadron of Army bombers which on April 18, 1942, bombed the Japanese mainland from the sea, taking off from a carrier, the *USS Hornet*. On the day after the raid, he was promoted to Brigadier General.

In July 1942 he was assigned to the 8th Air Force in England, later commanded the 12th Air Force in Africa, and in March 1943 became Commanding General, North African Strategic Air Forces. The following November he became Commanding General of the 15th Air Force and on January 1, 1944, was named to command the 8th Air Force in the European Theatre of Operations. In March 1944 he was promoted to Lieutenant General.

On January 5, 1946, he returned to the Shell Oil Company as Vice President. He was appointed by President Truman in 1952 as Chairman of the President's Airport Commission, and in 1958 became Chairman of the Board of Space Technology Laboratories, serving in that capacity until his retirement in 1962.

For major contributions to aeronautics leading to important advances in airplane design, flight research, and airline operation; particularly for the presentation of new methods for operational control and for the development of scientific and systematic methods in the flight testing of aircraft for basic design and performance data.

EDMUND TURNEY ALLEN

The Daniel Guggenheim Medal for 1943 was posthumously awarded to an outstanding representative of that small company of bold and devoted men who risk their lives—and sometimes, as in his case, forfeited it—in order that the age of flight might continue its unceasing and spectacular advance.

Edmund Turney Allen was born in Chicago, January 4, 1896. His father died in 1913, and a good part of his early education was self-obtained. He was graduated from high school in Chicago in 1913, and two years later matriculated at the University of Illinois.

Soon after the United States entered World War I, he enlisted and joined the officers' training camp at Fort Sheridan. Holding the rank of Lieutenant in the Signal Corps, Aviation Section, he served as a pilot instructor in 1916. In 1918 he conducted flight tests at Martlesham Heath in England. The next year found him flight-testing at McCook Field.

After the Armistice he spent a year at the University of Illinois and two years at the Massachusetts Institute of Technology. During the summers he acted as chief test pilot for the National Advisory Committee for Aeronautics at Langley Field. From 1920 to 1922 he was engaged at MIT in designing, building and flying gliders, two of which he flew in competition in France and Germany.

In 1924 he again served as test pilot at McCook Field, and from 1925 to 1929 flew the mail for United Air Lines. In 1930 he joined the Boeing Airplane Company as test pilot and the next year was test pilot for the Northrop Corporation. Then, in turn, he became consulting engineer and test pilot for Chance Vought Aircraft, Pan American Grace Airways (where he set a world's altitude record for standard commercial passenger planes of 29,800 feet), Eastern Air Lines, Curtiss-Wright Corporation, Douglas Aircraft Company, North American Aviation, Lockheed Aircraft Corporation, Stearman Airplane Company, Sikorsky Aircraft, Pratt & Whitney Aircraft, Spartan Aircraft Company, and Consolidated Aircraft Corporation. In 1939 he rejoined the Boeing Airplane Company, where he became Director of Flight and Aerodynamics.

Recognized as the leading American test pilot of his day, Allen was first recipient of the Octave Chanute Award, given annually by the Institute of the Aeronautical Sciences. On December 17, 1942, he delivered the Wright Brothers Lecture in New York, presenting a paper on "Flight Testing for Performance and Stability".

Less than a year later, on September 18, 1943, he was killed in the crash of a new Army bomber he was testing. The Guggenheim Medal and its accompanying scroll were presented to Mrs. Allen in Seattle on behalf of the Board of Award by Philip G. Johnson, then president of the Boeing Airplane Company. The plane which had been under test became the B-29, noted combat weapon of World War II. The presentation ceremony marked the opening of a laboratory constructed by the Boeing Company and named in Allen's memory.

For achievement in design and construction of military aircraft and for outstanding contributions to the methods of production.

LAWRENCE DALE BELL

Lawrence Dale Bell's first employment in aeronautics was as a mechanic for two well-known exhibition pilots: his brother, Grover E. Bell, killed in an accident in 1913, and Lincoln Beachy. He lived to become known all over the world for his own notable contributions to aircraft progress.

Born on April 5, 1895, at Mentone, Indiana, he was eighteen when he first became associated with aviation. Less than a year later he made his first plane: a bomber constructed for Mexico's famous Pancho Villa out of a converted Martin exhibition plane.

After his brother's death Bell began work as a factory hand for Glenn L. Martin. When the superintendent quit one day, young Bell suggested that he be given the job. In this manner, at 20, Bell became superintendent of an aircraft factory.

He left Martin in the late 20's to join Consolidated Aircraft Corporation in Buffalo, New York, becoming Vice-President and General Manager of that company in 1929.

When the company was moved to San Diego, Bell decided to stay in Buffalo and organize his own enterprise. The Bell Aircraft Corporation was formed there in 1935.

During the company's early days payrolls were met by taking surplus contracts from established companies. Bell's ideas, however, soon turned toward research, development and production. His concept of a new military plane was incorporated in the Airacuda, a twin-engine multi-place long range fighter with pusher-type engines, carrying two flexible 37 mm cannons. This experimental airplane was followed within a year by the P-39 Airacobra, a smaller, faster fighter. Bell was soon engaged in a large plant expansion to produce World War II fighter aircraft, including the Airacobra; the P-63 Kingcobra; the P-59 Airacomet, first jet-propelled plane produced in the United States; and the RP-63 armored airplane.

For years Bell had been an ardent advocate of rotary-wing aircraft. In 1941 Arthur M. Young, who had devoted a dozen years to helicopter research, visited him in Buffalo. Bell set him up in a shop near Buffalo, and spent hours with him developing his plans. Subsequently, Bell helicopters operated in many parts of the world, and performed yeoman service in the Korean war.

When Bell subsequently was requested to submit a proposal for an experimental airplane to attack the "sound barrier", he cautioned his engineers to "throw the books away". In this experiment, he insisted, no previous aircraft ideas or practices should be allowed to hamper creative imagination. The resulting X-1, the Air Force's first rocket-propelled airplane to be built for flight research by the NACA, was the first man-carrying vehicle to exceed the speed of sound.

Bell died at Buffalo, New York, on October 20, 1956.

MEDALIST FOR 1945

For outstanding contributions to the development of civil and military aircraft, and for notable achievement in assuring the success of our wartime aircraft production program.

THEODORE PAUL WRIGHT

Distinguished in many fields of aeronautics, Theodore Paul Wright in his unusual career combined the technical contributions of a skilled engineer and scientist with the practical talents of production expert, research manager, university official and government administrator.

Born at Galesburg, Illinois, on May 25, 1895, he was graduated from Lombard College in 1915, received the Bachelor of Science degree from Massachusetts Institute of Technology in 1918, and joined the United States Naval Reserve Flying Corps as an ensign. In 1919 he was promoted to Lieutenant, Junior Grade, and to Lieutenant in 1920.

After leaving the Navy, he joined the Curtiss Aeroplane & Motor Company, Inc., as Executive Engineer. In 1925 he became Chief Engineer of the Airplane Division of the Company, and under his supervision many notable aircraft were produced, among them the Hawk, Falcon, Hell Diver, Shrike and Condor, and such civilian craft as the Robin, Fledgling, King Bird and commercial Condor, as well as the Curtiss Tanager, which won the $100,000 Guggenheim Safe Aircraft Competition in 1929.

In June 1940 he was called to Washington to serve with the Advisory Committee for the Council of National Defense to program the acceleration of aircraft production. In February 1941 he was named Assistant Chief of the Aircraft Branch of the Office of Production Management, which became the War Production Board. When the Aircraft Resources Control Office was established in March 1943, Wright became its Director. It was this office which was called upon by the President to direct the procurement of 50,000 planes per year, at the time considered a fantastic goal. It was not only accomplished, however, but the original production rate was doubled.

Wright's appointment as Administrator of Civil Aeronautics was announced on September 20, 1944. In November of that year he served as technical secretary of the International Civil Aviation Conference in Chicago. As CAA Administrator he established the Non-scheduled Flying Advisory Committee, and was active in the program for improved aids to air navigation and instrument landing, and airport development. In the same period he was Director of the Aircraft Division of the United States Strategic Bombing Survey, and also served as Vice Chairman of the National Advisory Committee for Aeronautics and Chairman of its Aerodynamics Committee.

He resigned from the CAA in 1948 to become Vice-President for Research at Cornell University, and President of the Cornell Aeronautical Laboratory at Buffalo, in which capacities he served until his retirement in 1960. He was Acting President of Cornell from February 1, 1951 to July 1, 1951, and was Chairman of the Executive Committee of the Daniel and Florence Guggenheim Aviation Safety Center at Cornell from its founding in 1950 until 1961.

For pioneering the development of turbojet propulsion of aircraft.

SIR FRANK WHITTLE

One day in July 1942, during World War II, a slightly-built young Englishman arrived in Washington on a highly confidential mission. So important was the equipment that accompanied him, so vital its secret, that he traveled under an assumed name and many who met him knew him only as "Frank."

He was in fact Frank Whittle, then a Wing Commander in the Royal Air Force; pioneer of the turbojet engine which was destined to make one of the most profound changes in aircraft propulsion since the beginning of powered flight. Born in Coventry, England, on June 1, 1907, Whittle entered Leamington College at the age of 11 on a scholarship won in elementary school. At the age of 16 he entered the Royal Air Force as an aircraft apprentice in the trade of metal rigger. At the final examination he was granted a cadetship at the Royal Air Force College, Cranwell.

During 1928 and 1929, as a pilot officer, he spent fifteen months in the 111th

Fighter Squadron and was then assigned to a flying instructors' course at the Central Flying School, Wittering. It was during this course that the idea of using the turbine for jet propulsion first occurred to him. His patent application was filed in January, 1930.

After one year as flying instructor and eighteen months as a floatplane and catapult test pilot, he was sent to Henlow in 1932 to take the Officers Engineering Course. The summer of 1934 saw him at Cambridge University (Peterhouse). At the end of two years he was graduated as a Bachelor of Arts with First Class Honours in the Mechanical Science tripos.

With the aid of two former officers of the Royal Air Force, R. D. Williams and J. C. B. Tinling, a company named Power Jets Ltd. was formed in March 1936, and an order was placed with the British Thomson-Houston Company at Rugby for the manufacture of an experimental jet propulsion turbine. In 1936 the Air Ministry arranged for Whittle to remain at Cambridge for a post-graduate year, enabling him to continue work on the engine. Later, after the Whittle engine had successfully passed its first test run, the Ministry permitted him to work full time on it by assigning him to the Special Duty List, on which he remained until 1946.

In May 1941 the Gloster-Whittle E-28, powered by the W-2 engine, flew successfully. In October 1941 an experimental edition of the engine and drawings were sent to the General Electric Company in the United States. Nine months later Whittle himself made his secret visit.

He was made a Knight Commander of the Order of the British Empire in July 1948. He retired from the Royal Air Force with the rank of Air Commodore later the same year. After four years as technical advisor to BOAC he turned his attention to the design and development of a turbo-drill for oil wells, first in association with Shell, and later with Bristol Siddeley Engines. He became a Fellow of the Royal Society in 1947.

For outstanding achievement in advancing aeronautics, particularly for his conception and organization of the Institute of the Aeronautical Sciences.

LESTER DURAND GARDNER

The contribution of Lester Durand Gardner to the advancement of the age of flight was unique: the creation of the Institute of the Aeronautical Sciences, later the Institute of the Aerospace Sciences, which continues its force into the space age as one of the two progenitors of the American Institute of Aeronautics and Astronautics, the other being the American Rocket Society.

Born in New York City on August 7, 1876, Gardner was graduated from Massachusetts Institute of Technology as Bachelor of Science in 1898. After a year of graduate study in Administrative Law at Columbia University, he was employed successively on the editorial staffs of the *New York Times, New York Tribune, New York Sun, Collier's Magazine* and other publications.

In the early days of radio broadcasting, he gave weekly talks on the progress of aviation. He rebroadcast observations made from an airplane during an eclipse of the sun, and arranged for the first demonstration of ship-to-shore radio telephone with David Sarnoff, later head of the Radio Corporation of America, as radio operator. In 1915, with the encouragement of Glenn L. Martin, Grover Loening and Jerome C. Hunsaker, he organized the Gardner Publishing Company, which started *Aviation, Who's Who in American Aeronautics*, and *The Rubber Age*.

When the United States entered World War I, Gardner became, in 1917, a Lieutenant in the Aviation Section of the Signal Corps. He was soon promoted to a captaincy in the regular Army, and while on duty at Kelly Field, Texas, organized 89 aero squadrons for overseas service. Ordered to Washington to serve on the Control Board of the U.S. Air Service, he was promoted to Major. Taking flying instruction at Bolling Field, he was on flying status when discharged from the Army in 1918.

It was in 1932 that Gardner and several friends who were leaders in American aviation organized the Institute of the Aeronautical Sciences. He was its executive officer for fourteen years.

From a modest beginning, the Institute of the Aeronautical Sciences grew rapidly. Gardner started publication of the *Journal of the Aeronautical Sciences* and *The Aeronautical Engineering Review* for the Institute. Various contributions of funds amounting to over $2,000,000, and valuable historical treasures came to the Institute as a result of his efforts. In 1942 the Daniel Guggenheim estate on Long Island was given to the IAS by Mrs. Florence Guggenheim. In 1945 the Institute purchased the residence of E. J. Berwind at the corner of Fifth Avenue and 64th Street, New York, which it remodeled and occupied as its headquarters. Other buildings in Los Angeles and San Diego were built for the Institute from endowments.

Gardner retired as Chairman of the Council of the Institute in 1946, but continued his interest in the organization until his death, on November 23, 1956, in New York City.

For outstanding achievement in successfully advancing aircraft design, both for Naval and peacetime use.

LEROY RANDLE GRUMMAN

Vice-Admiral John McCain, one of the Navy's great fighting admirals, once remarked: "The name Grumman on a plane is like sterling on silver."

The name is that of Leroy Randle Grumman, who was born at Huntington, New York, on January 4, 1895, worked his way through Cornell University, and for the three subsequent years served in the Navy as a pilot in World War I. Returning to civilian life he became General Manager of the Loening Aeronautical Corporation. In 1929 he formed the Grumman Aircraft Engineering Corporation at Bethpage, Long Island, with a total capital of $67,000. Grumman served as President of the company until 1946, when he became Chairman of the Board.

The company obtained its first Navy contract—for two amphibian floats— at $33,700. A contract for an experimental fighting plane followed. This was the first

Navy fighter with retractable landing wheels, and its speed of 206 miles per hour caused a sensation. Grumman also began building amphibians for sportsmen and corporation executives. By 1939, Grumman had 700 employees. When war came, expansion was rapid.

The Grumman folding wing fighters of the "cat" family served a vital purpose in saving space, thus multiplying the carrier's striking force. To solve the problem of a folding wing which would be practical and also rugged when unfolded, Grumman is said to have made no theoretical drawings, but instead took drawing paper, a gum eraser, a pencil, and some paper clips and worked with these until he had arrived at the solution.

The first Hellcat was built in August 1942. The hierarchy of the "cats": the Wildcat, the Hellcat, the Bearcat and the twin-engine Tiger Cat, wrote a continuing story of triumph in the Pacific. In the first five months of 1944, Navy pilots destroyed 444 enemy planes in the air and another 323 on the ground. In the great air battle off the Marianas, Hellcat pilots brought down 365 Japanese planes in one day. Hellcats, Wildcats, and Avengers proved potent weapons against U-boats in the Atlantic. The Wildcats flew from baby flattops and, together with the rocket-firing Avengers, destroyed 31 German submarines in one six-month period.

Following World War II's propeller-driven aircraft, Grumman's first jet fighter was the F9F-5 Panther which, in encounters with the Russian MIG-15 in Korea, accounted for 15 of the enemy without loss. Following the Panther came the famous Cougar and Tiger series of fighters, and the F111B variable-sweep-wing airplane for the United States Navy. Grumman aircraft also include the A-6A Intruder attack aircraft, the E-2A Hawkeye, the OV-1 Mohawk, the S-2D Tracker, the HU16 Albatross amphibian and the Gulfstream corporate transport.

In space flight developments, the Grumman company is responsible for the design, development and construction of the Lunar Excursion Module (LEM) designed to land the first American astronauts on the moon.

*For pioneering in research and a
continuous record of contributions
to the art and science of aeronautics.*

EDWARD PEARSON WARNER

Few men have been able to contribute to the arts and sciences of flight in so many
ways as Edward Pearson Warner, researcher in many fields, teacher, writer, developer of government air policy, member of the Civil Aeronautics Board, and president of the International Civil Aviation Organization.

Born in Pittsburgh, Pennsylvania, on November 9, 1894, Warner was graduated from Harvard in 1916 and from Massachusetts Institute of Technology
in 1917. When the United States entered World War I, he was appointed an
assistant in aeronautical engineering at MIT. At the War's end, he became Chief
Physicist of the National Advisory Committee for Aeronautics. He returned to
MIT in 1920 and for five years mingled teaching of airplane design with writing
and consulting.

He initiated the drafting of the Massachusetts Aeronautical Act of 1920 and served as chairman of the State Advisory Board on Aeronautics and of the Boston Municipal Air Board. In 1924–1925 he acted as consultant to the United States Air Mail Service, and in 1925 was consultant to the President's Aircraft Board, better known as the Morrow Board.

In 1926 he was appointed Assistant Secretary of the Navy for Aeronautics, in which position he served for three years. He was active on several committees of the Daniel Guggenheim Fund for the Promotion of Aeronautics. He subsequently became editor of *Aviation*; held various offices, including the presidency, in the Society of Automotive Engineers, and was one of the Founders of the Institute of the Aeronautical Sciences.

In July 1934 President Franklin D. Roosevelt appointed him a member of the Federal Aviation Commission, which he served as Vice Chairman. In November 1938 he joined the staff of the Civil Aeronautics Authority, and five months later was appointed a member. He retained membership in the Authority and its successor, the Civil Aeronautics Board, for more than six years, serving as Vice Chairman of the CAB for 1941 and for the years 1943–45. He was a member of the NACA from 1929 until 1945.

During a visit he made to England in 1944, discussion with British Government authorities led to the calling of the International Civil Aviation Conference in Chicago in November of that year. Named to represent the United States on the provisional organization's Council, he attended the first meeting and was elected President.

Under Warner's presidency, the International Civil Aviation Organization grew to include almost all the nations of the world that take substantial part in international air navigation. It developed standards for such navigational services as meteorology, air traffic control and communications, and produced regional plans for the installation and operation of air navigation facilities over most of the globe. Warner retired from the Presidency in 1957, and died on July 11, 1958, at Duxbury, Massachusetts.

For outstanding leadership in aeronautical research and fundamental contributions to aeronautical science.

HUGH LATIMER DRYDEN

Hardly a phase of the rapidly developing flight sciences exists which has not been materially shaped and enhanced by the research and administrative career of Hugh Latimer Dryden.

Born July 2, 1898, at Pocomoke City, Maryland, he earned his way through The Johns Hopkins University. Greatly influenced by Dr. Joseph S. Ames, one of the pioneers in aerodynamics, he did his graduate work in physics, receiving his Ph.D. from Johns Hopkins in 1919.

At the age of 21, Dryden was named Chief of the Aerodynamics Section of the Bureau of Standards. In 1924, with L. J. Briggs, he made some of the earliest measurements of the aerodynamic characteristics of airfoils near the speed of sound. Five years later, with A. M. Kuethe, he published the first of a series of important papers on the measurement of turbulence.

In 1934 he was made chief of the Mechanics and Sound division of the Bureau of Standards, and in January 1946 Assistant Director of the Bureau. In the same year he was promoted to Associate Director. During the second World War he was charged with guiding development of Bat, the radar-homing missile used by the Navy against the Japanese. He also served on committees dealing with guided missiles under the sponsorship of the Joint Chiefs of Staff, the NACA, the Ordnance Department of the Army, and the Army Air Forces. After the war he continued to take an important part in the missile development program of the Bureau of Standards.

In September 1947, after more than 29 years of service there, Dryden left the Bureau of Standards to become Director of Aeronautical Research of the National Advisory Committee for Aeronautics. In 1949 his responsibilities were again increased: he became Director of NACA.

The launching of Sputnik I by the Soviet Union on October 4, 1957, led to intensive consideration of the objectives of the United States in the exploration and exploitation of space, and of the form of organization required to realize these objectives. On July 29, 1958, the National Aeronautics and Space Act established a new civilian agency, the National Aeronautics and Space Administration, terminating NACA and transferring its functions to the new agency. Dryden was named Deputy Administrator of NASA by President Eisenhower and continued to serve in this capacity under President Kennedy.

In addition to his other duties, Dryden served as a member of many scientific committees advising government agencies, including the Department of Defense and the military services. He was adviser to the Science Advisory Committee to the President, a member of the Standing Committee of the Federal Council on Science and Technology, a member of the Defense Science Board, Technical Adviser to the U.S. Representative on the United Nations Committee on the Peaceful Uses of Outer Space, and national delegate to the NATO Advisory Group for Aeronautical Research and Development.

*For a lifetime of outstanding con-
tributions to aeronautics, including
pioneering with multi-engine airplanes, flying boats, amphibians
and helicopters.*

IGOR IVAN SIKORSKY

Igor Ivan Sikorsky, destined to become world-famous for his rotary-wing aircraft and large-scale multi-engined airplanes and flying boats, was born May 25, 1889, in Kiev, Russia. Graduating from the Naval College in Petrograd in 1906, he went to Paris to study engineering, returning a year later to continue his education at the Mechanical Engineering College of the Polytechnical Institute in Kiev.

During 1909–1910 he designed and built his first and second helicopters. The following three years Sikorsky constructed several types of airplanes and taught himself to fly. Of his early aircraft, the S-6 received the highest award during the Moscow Aviation Exhibition in 1912, and later the same year took first prize in a military competition in St. Petersburg. In 1913 he designed, built and successfully piloted the first four-engined airplane ever produced. He designed and built several four-engined bombers during 1914–1917, the first large aircraft successfully used during World War I.

After the Russian Revolution of 1917 he went to France, to build large bombers for the French Government. Following the Armistice he came to the United States. In 1923 the Sikorsky Aero Engineering Corporation was organized here, and in 1924 completed a successful twin-engine, eighteen-passenger, all-metal cabin land-plane, the S-29A. More new types of airplanes followed, among them the S-38, first successful twin-engine amphibian. This aircraft carried the first airmail between continental United States and the Panama Canal, and was extensively used by several American airlines in pioneering and establishing South American, Hawaiian and other passenger routes.

The company was acquired by the United Aircraft Corporation in 1929. Continuing to operate as the Sikorsky Division, in 1931 it produced for Pan American Airways the first large four-engined Flying Clipper, the S-40. Later the company produced a series of trans-oceanic Flying Clipper ships, of which the S-42 pioneered regular trans-oceanic flights from America and was the first aircraft to carry regular mail from the United States across the Pacific and Atlantic Oceans.

The VS-300 helicopter, built by Sikorsky in 1939, proved to be the first practical direct-lift aircraft in the western hemisphere. This helicopter virtually started the helicopter industry in the United States. There followed a series of successful helicopters of various sizes which were the first to be used by any Allied power during World War II, and which proved extremely useful during the Korean conflict. As a result, the helicopter was established as a novel and valuable type of aircraft for a great variety of military as well as commercial uses. It has also proved to be an exceptionally useful and efficient means of saving lives, under many difficult conditions.

Sikorsky retired as Engineering Manager of the Division in 1957 but continues as advisor and consultant.

For forty years of pioneering in military and commercial aircraft and the development of long-range jet transport.

SIR GEOFFREY DE HAVILLAND

From early hand-built biplanes to successful jet transports, the career of Sir Geoffrey de Havilland has spanned the whole developmental period of aeronautics.

Born in England July 27, 1882, he received his education at St. Edwards, Oxford, and The Crystal Palace School of Engineering. As a young man of 26, he left a position in the motor industry in London to satisfy an overwhelming desire to build an airplane and fly it. His first aircraft was a biplane powered by a 45-horsepower engine of his own design. It crashed on its first flight, but a simpler aircraft was built around the same engine, and with this in the summer of 1910 he taught himself to fly.

A few months later de Havilland joined the Army Balloon Factory at Farnborough. He was responsible for the design, early in 1911, of a canard machine for the Army, and a tractor biplane, the Bleriot Experimental No. 1, forerunner of the B.E. 2 used early in World War I. In May 1914 he joined The Aircraft Manufacturing Co., Ltd.

as Chief Designer and pilot. His initial design there was the D.H. 1 two-seat pusher biplane fighter, first in the series of de Havilland aircraft. Throughout World War I, de Havilland was responsible for a number of military aircraft, notably the D.H. 4 (Rolls-Royce Eagle), the D.H. 9 (Siddeley Puma) and the D.H. 10 twin-engined bomber. By 1918, a third of the total Allied air strength was comprised of airplanes of de Havilland design.

De Havilland founded The de Havilland Aircraft Co., Ltd., in 1920, and started activities in a small way at Stag Lane, Edgware, northwest London. The first scheduled air service between London and Paris was inaugurated with de Havilland D.H. 4A and D.H. 16 two-passenger and four-passenger aircraft. Thereafter de Havilland created a number of successful airliners for the British Empire services, notably the single-engined D.H. 34 and D.H. 50 and the three-engine Hercules D.H. 66. In the 1920's he pioneered the light airplane with his Moth, which he first flew on February 22, 1925.

World War II led de Havilland again into the military field. He conceived the idea of the high-speed general-purpose Mosquito, an outstanding combat craft, which was fastest in the fray for two and a half years. By early 1941 he had a jet engine, the Goblin, running on test. The company's extensive military experience made possible the introduction after the war of the first jet airliner, the famous Comet.

De Havilland was awarded the Air Force Cross for his services to military aviation; was appointed a Commander of the Order of the British Empire in 1934, was knighted in 1944, and was awarded the Order of Merit in 1962. As Technical Director, he was the leader of the de Havilland enterprise until his retirement in 1955.

CHARLES AUGUSTUS LINDBERGH

Seldom has any man caught and held such long-time world-wide attention and respect as Charles Augustus Lindbergh, whose solo non-stop flight across the Atlantic on May 20–21, 1927, electrified all the peoples of the globe.

Born in Detroit, Michigan, on February 4, 1902, he entered the University of Wisconsin in 1920. He left college in 1922 and enrolled in a flying school at Lincoln, Nebraska. He received instruction first from Ira Biffle; later from E. G. Bahl and Harold Lynch. He accompanied the latter two pilots on barnstorming trips, as mechanic, wing-walker, and parachute-jumper.

During a night air-mail flight in the fall of 1926, after reading of Raymond Orteig's offer of a $25,000 prize, he first considered a non-stop flight from New York to Paris. After many difficulties, he obtained financial backing and purchased a Ryan monoplane with a single engine, at San Diego, California. He took off from San Diego on May 10, 1927, and after a stopover at St. Louis, reached Curtiss Field, Long Island, on May 12, establishing new records.

On May 20, 1927, he left Roosevelt Field, Long Island, on the 3,600-mile flight which ended at Le Bourget airport, Paris, the following day. This pioneering achievement brought world-wide praise and spectacular receptions in Paris, Brussels, London, Washington, New York, and St. Louis. Subsequently he made an air tour of the United States under the auspices of the Daniel Guggenheim Fund for the Promotion of Aeronautics.

As technical advisor to Transcontinental Air Transport and Pan American Airways, he then surveyed new domestic and Latin-American air routes. He explored the great-circle Arctic route to Asia and the Greenland-Iceland route to Europe. Mrs. Lindbergh, the former Anne Spencer Morrow, whom he married on May 27, 1929, accompanied her husband on many of these flights.

In December 1935, following the kidnapping and death of their oldest son, the Lindberghs went to live in England, and later moved to France. Invited to Germany to view the development of the German air force, the flier gave the American Government valuable information on the strength and condition of the Luftwaffe.

Returning to the United States in the spring of 1939, he went on active duty with the Air Corps, in which he held the rank of Colonel. In 1944 he went to the Pacific theater of operations as a civilian technician. Following the capitulation of Germany he spent two months with a United States Navy mission to study German developments in jet aircraft, rocket and guided missile warfare.

After the war he served as a consultant for the Air Force, visiting various bases in America, Europe, Africa, Asia, and the Pacific.

MEDALIST FOR 1954

For initiating and organizing commercial air routes and services, promoting aeronautical research, development and production of aircraft and engines, and advancing the art of aeronautics.

CLARENCE DECATUR HOWE

A Canadian citizen by choice, Clarence Decatur Howe contributed much to the emergence of Canada as an industrial nation and particularly to the development of her transportation and communication systems.

Born January 15, 1886, at Waltham, Massachusetts, he received the degree of Bachelor of Science from the Massachusetts Institute of Technology in 1907 and immediately joined the staff as an instructor. In 1908, recommended by the Institute, he was appointed Professor of Civil Engineering at Dalhousie University, Halifax. Five years later he became Chief Engineer of the Board of Grain Commissioners, having supervision of the construction of grain elevators. In 1916 he formed his own firm, C. D. Howe and Company, and during the following twenty years built grain elevators, docks and factories, became a recognized expert on elevator construction, and acquired a fortune.

In 1935 Howe was elected to the House of Commons and joined the Cabinet as Minister of Railways and Canals, and Minister of Marine. Merging these departments and the Civil Aviation Branch of the Department of National Defence, he next year became Minister of Transport, established the National Harbours Board and the Canadian Broadcasting Commission, and reorganized the administration of the Canadian National Railways.

Recognizing the vital importance of air transportation to Canada—where by the early thirties more air freight was being carried than in any other country— and the need of interurban and transcontinental air services, Howe introduced the Trans Canada Air Lines Act, which passed in 1937. Having already initiated the provision of ground and operating services, he pressed forward with all the resources at his command. To focus public attention on his favorite project he made a dawn-to-dusk flight from Montreal to Vancouver in July. By 1940 regular transcontinental passenger services were operating.

With the outbreak of war, Howe became Minister of Munitions and Supply, and directed the vast industrial war effort. He provided more than 100 ground installations and thousands of aircraft for the British Commonwealth Air Training Plan, developed an industry which produced over 13,000 aircraft, the greatest per capita output in the free world, and built great aerodromes for ferrying bombers overseas and for defense units on the coasts.

While he was Minister of Reconstruction and Supply, in 1944, Turbo Research Limited, a Crown company, was organized for research and development of gas turbines. Later, as a commercial firm, it designed the Orenda and produced nearly 3800 of these aircraft engines installed in nearly 700 Canuck twin-jet long-range all-weather fighters and in many of the 1800 Sabres built in Canada for the Royal Canadian Air Force.

Howe was serving as Minister of Trade and Commerce when, after more than twenty years in power, the Government was defeated in 1957. He died at Montreal, December 31, 1960.

MEDALIST FOR 1955

For long-continued leadership in the development of aerodynamic theory and its application to the practical problems of flight, in education in the aeronautical sciences, and in stimulating international cooperation in aeronautical research.

THEODORE VON KÁRMÁN

Theodore von Kárm án, sometimes called the father of modern aerodynamics, was born in Budapest, Hungary, May 11, 1881, and was graduated as a mechanical engineer from the Budapest Technical University in 1902. In 1906 he enrolled as an advanced student at the University of Göttingen, one of his teachers being Ludwig Prandtl, and received his PhD degree in 1908. In 1912 he became Professor of Aeronautics and Mechanics at the University of Aachen and head of that University's Aeronautical Institute.

In 1926 the Guggenheim Fund for the Promotion of Aeronautics brought von Kármán to the United States for a series of lectures and to advise on the design of the Guggenheim Aeronautical Laboratories at California Institute of Technology. He returned in 1928 to act as Research Associate at Caltech, and in 1930 became Director of the Guggenheim Aeronautical Laboratories.

At Caltech he headed the Army Air Corps Jet Propulsion Project, later sponsored jointly by the Air Force and the Ordnance Department. His ideas started research on the Bell X-1, the first plane to break the sound barrier. He became consultant to the Army Air Forces and advisor to the Wright-Patterson Air Force Base. The Army Ordnance Department also began utilizing his services in 1938. When the Scientific Advisory Committee was founded in 1940 he became a member. In 1944 he organized the Scientific Advisory Group of the Army Air Forces, later the Air Force Scientific Advisory Board, and was its chairman until 1954.

In the early 1940's he tried to persuade American corporations to manufacture rockets for the Armed Forces. None was interested, so von Kármán and four Caltech associates raised $8,700 and started the Aerojet Engineering Corporation (now Aerojet-General Corporation) in Azusa, California. By 1963 Aerojet-General had become one of the country's 100 largest industrial corporations.

Von Kármán became Professor Emeritus at California Institute of Technology in 1949. On his recommendation the Scientific Advisory Board sponsored a meeting of the major aeronautical research establishments of NATO countries, and out of this came NATO's Advisory Group for Aeronautical Research and Development (AGARD), with von Kármán as Chairman. He was President of Honor of the International Union of Theoretical and Applied Mechanics, a member of the International Council of the Aeronautical Sciences, and Director of the International Academy of Astronautics. He was the first recipient of the National Medal of Science, presented to him by President Kennedy on February 18, 1963.

Von Kármán made important contributions to applied mathematics, physics, strength of materials, stress analysis, theory of elasticity, monocoque structures, vibrations, mechanics of ideal, viscous, and compressible fluids, turbulence, aerodynamics of aircraft, hydrodynamics of planing surfaces, and heat transfer. Many theories bear his name, such as the Kármán Vortex Street, formulated in 1911. He died on May 7, 1963, at Aachen, Germany.

For a wide range of major achieve-
ments throughout a lifetime devoted
to aviation, with specific reference
to his many notable contributions
to the vital aircraft engine field.

FREDERICK BRANT RENTSCHLER

Frederick Brant Rentschler was a man who "thought, talked, breathed, and dreamed engines."

Born in Butler County, Ohio, on November 8, 1887, he was graduated from Princeton University in 1909. At the outbreak of World War I he enlisted in the Army Air Service, was commissioned a First Lieutenant and assigned to an airplane engine plant in New Brunswick, New Jersey. Later, as a Captain, he was put in charge of production at the Wright-Martin plant, manufacturing engines for the French Government.

By the war's end, Rentschler had come to realize that his first love was aircraft engines. Approached to help organize the Wright Aeronautical Corporation, he became its Vice President and General Manager, and shortly thereafter its President. The new company in the early 1920s launched its air-cooled engine line, from which later developed the successful Whirlwind engines. One of these powered Lindbergh's *Spirit of St. Louis.*

By 1924 Rentschler had become convinced that the future of aviation lay in the design and development of still bigger and better powerplants, of the radial air-cooled configuration. He resigned from the Wright Aeronautical Corporation and on July 14, 1925, assumed the principal role in the formation of the Pratt & Whitney Aircraft Company, with himself as President, in Hartford, Connecticut. By December 24 of that year the first Pratt & Whitney aircraft engine was completed, the now famous Wasp. By 1929 the Wasp and a later engine, the Hornet, were recognized as prime factors in bringing the nation's military aviation to world leadership. The Wasp was also aiding in the rapid development of commercial airline operations.

Successful associations with Boeing and Vought led in 1928 to the formation of the United Aircraft & Transport Corporation, which included Pratt & Whitney Aircraft Company, Boeing, Hamilton Standard (propellers), Stearman, Sikorsky Aircraft, Chance Vought, and United Air Lines. Rentschler was elected President of the new company. In 1934 another reorganization saw three independent groups emerge: United Air Lines, Boeing, and United Aircraft. Rentschler became Chairman and chief executive officer of United Aircraft.

President Roosevelt's request for 50,000 planes a year in the military program of World War II brought a new challenge. Rentschler worked out a plan for licensing automobile manufacturers to produce military engines. Through this arrangement the greatly expanded Pratt & Whitney Aircraft Company and its licensees built approximately 50 per cent of the engines used by the combined Air Forces of the United States in World War II.

In the ten years following the war, Rentschler had broad direction of Pratt & Whitney Aircraft's highly successful transition from piston to jet powerplants. He died April 25, 1956, at his winter home in Boca Raton, Florida.

For the development of a long line of successful civil and military aircraft and for notable contributions to aeronautics in public service.

ARTHUR EMMONS RAYMOND

Arthur Emmons Raymond, engineer and developer of many famous aircraft, was born March 24, 1899, in Boston, Massachusetts, and grew up in Pasadena, California, where his father owned the Raymond Hotel. He was graduated from Harvard in 1920, and in 1921 received the M.S. degree in aeronautical engineering from Massachusetts Institute of Technology.

Returning to California, Raymond first went into the hotel business with his father, but took courses in structures at the California Institute of Technology and in 1925 accepted a shop job with the Douglas Aircraft Company in Santa Monica. A few weeks later, Donald Douglas, needing a good man in stress analysis, asked Edward P. Warner at MIT to recommend his best student in that field. Warner wired back: "He is Arthur Raymond. He works in your shop."

Douglas immediately transferred Raymond to the task of analyzing stresses in a pontoon strut in the Douglas Aircraft Company's engineering department, consisting of about a dozen engineers including Douglas himself. In 1927 Raymond was promoted to Assistant Chief Engineer, and became Chief Engineer in 1936.

Under Raymond, an impressive list of aircraft was developed, including the DC series from DC-1 to the jet-powered DC-8; the B-19; the A-20 (Havoc) attack bomber and its successor the A-26; the Navy's "Dauntless" (SBD) dive bomber; the TBD torpedo-bomber series, and 39 other experimental types, including a line of guided missiles.

From 1927 until 1934 Raymond also served as Assistant Professor of Aeronautics at California Institute of Technology, and there followed closely the wind-tunnel tests of the DC-2 transport and other outstanding aircraft. In 1939 he became Vice President in Charge of Engineering at Douglas.

Apart from the aircraft developments associated with his company, Raymond has given many other valuable services to aviation. During World War II he undertook studies for the Secretary of War relating to the bombing of Japan. In 1954 he was appointed a member of the Kelly Committee to study the defense of the nation against atomic attack. He has served as a member of the Steering Group of the Technical Advisory Panel of Aeronautics of the Department of Defense, and as a member of the National Advisory Committee for Aeronautics.

In 1951 he gave the Wilbur Wright Memorial Lecture, his subject being "Well-Tempered Aircraft", in which he described the factors responsible for the success of some aircraft designs and the failure of others.

Following his retirement from Douglas in 1960, he served as consultant to the President of The Rand Corporation and as Trustee of Aerospace Corporation. He also acted as a special consultant to James E. Webb, Administrator of NASA, and was a member of the Space Systems Division Advisory Group of the Air Force.

MEDALIST FOR 1958

For leadership and continuous personal participation over a quarter of a century in developing the equipment and operating techniques of air transport.

WILLIAM LITTLEWOOD

The British magazine *Aeroplane* once said of William Littlewood: "The industry has his genius to thank for much of the efficiency built into the aircraft that really put the air transport business on the map."

Born in New York City on October 21, 1898, he was graduated from Cornell University with a degree in mechanical engineering in 1920. Following positions with the Niles-Bement-Pond Company and Ingersoll-Rand Company he became production manager of the Fairchild-Caminez Engine Corporation in 1927. In the following year he became General Manager of the Fairchild Engine Company.

In June 1930 he moved to American Airways, Inc., which had been organized by the Aviation Corporation, and three years later became Chief Engineer. American Airlines succeeded American Airways in 1934, and in 1937 Littlewood became Vice President in Charge of Engineering. In addition to broad technical supervision of company matters, he was in charge of the specification and procurement of all new flying equipment used by American Airlines.

In 1934 American Airlines had introduced "sleeper planes" on transcontinental flights, using Condor biplanes. These were followed by improved all-metal airplanes, but the industry needed still larger, faster, more efficient transports. Littlewood prepared a set of specifications which were translated by Douglas engineers into the DC-3, the aircraft destined to transform the struggling young airline business into a profitable industry. American Airlines placed the first quantity order, and in July 1936 became the first DC-3 airline operator.

Littlewood made similar contributions to successive models of the Douglas DC series and the Consolidated Vultee Convair series, and was active in the development of all American turboprop and jet transports.

During World War II, he served as chairman of a committee of Air Force, Navy and civilian personnel charged with the standardization of air transport aircraft, an activity which greatly influenced post-war developments. He was for 10 years a member of the Executive Committee of the National Advisory Committee for Aeronautics, now the National Aeronautics and Space Administration. He was Chairman of the Advisory Panel on Aeronautics of the Office of the Assistant Secretary of Defense (Research and Engineering), and served on the Executive Committee of the Defense Science Board.

He has been President of the Society of Automotive Engineers and of the Institute of the Aerospace Sciences (now AIAA), which elected him an Honorary Fellow in 1957. He is permanent Vice Chairman of the Industry Advisory Committee of the Flight Safety Foundation. He is an Honorary Fellow of the Royal Aeronautical Society and a Fellow of the Canadian Aero Space Institute. He has written many technical articles and papers, and was Wright Brothers Lecturer in 1952.

MEDALIST FOR 1959

For a lifetime devoted to the design of military and commercial aircraft, culminating in the successful introduction into world-wide commercial service of the first turbine-powered propeller-driven aircraft.

SIR GEORGE EDWARDS

Destined to become one of the world's foremost aircraft designers and administrators, and to be knighted in 1957, George Robert Edwards was born July 9, 1908, in Highams Park, Essex, England. He received his technical education from the South West Essex Technical College and London University, and in 1935 joined the design staff of Vickers-Armstrongs, a leading aircraft manufacturing concern.

At the outbreak of World War II he became Experimental Manager at Vickers, and the projects of which he was in charge included some of the first British pressurized aircraft.

In 1945 he was appointed Chief Designer, with responsibility for Britain's first post-war transport, the Viking. More than 160 Vikings were built, and production of the Valetta and Varsity military versions brought production of Vickers' piston-engined transports to a total of 585.

Even as the Viking was coming into service, Edwards was talking of it as the "last of the piston-engined line." He was sure, while many others were still lukewarm, that a turbine-powered transport must be the next move in civil aviation. Under his direction Vickers built for the Ministry of Supply a special Viking powered by two Rolls-Royce Nene jets. In July 1948 this aircraft, the first jet transport to be built anywhere, flew to Paris in 34 minutes and seven seconds, at 385 miles per hour.

At the same time another Edwards aircraft, the Viscount, was also beginning its flights trials. The Viscount 630 prototype, powered by Rolls-Royce Dart propeller-turbines, introduced the world's first scheduled airline services by a turbine-engined aircraft, on July 29, 1950. The project encountered many doubts and obstructions, and it was not until 1953 that the first production-model Viscount 700s were delivered to British European Airways.

The first major sale of British airliners to North America came in November 1952, when Trans-Canada Air Lines placed an initial order for 15 Viscounts. Edwards personally headed the sales team. By this time, with his Vanguard, big brother of the Viscount, and his Valiant 4-jet bomber also flying, he was acknowledged on both sides of the Atlantic as a foremost aircraft designer and was appointed General Manager of the Vickers-Armstrongs Aircraft Division. In 1953 he became Managing Director. In June 1955 he was appointed to the Board of Vickers, Ltd. and also became Managing Director of the British Aircraft Corporation and Chairman of the four operating subsidiary companies, Bristol Aircraft, English Electric Aviation, Hunting Aircraft and Vickers-Armstrongs (Aircraft).

A fellow of the Royal Society of Arts, Sir George is a Member of the Order of the British Empire (1944), a Commander of the Order of the British Empire (1952) and winner of the British Gold Medal for Aeronautics (1952).

MEDALIST FOR 1960

For a lifetime devoted to the development of aeronautics in America.

GROVER LOENING

Pioneer, engineer, public servant—Grover Loening was born September 12, 1888, in Bremen, Germany, where his father was United States Consul-General. He received his B.A. from Columbia College in 1908, and M.A. in Aeronautics from Columbia University in 1910—the first such degree awarded in America. His M.A. thesis was subsequently published as "Monoplanes and Biplanes." He received the C.E. degree from Columbia in 1911.

After graduation, Loening joined the Queen Aeroplane Company in New York, building Bleriots for exhibition pilots. In 1912, he built his pioneer Aeroboat. In 1913 Orville Wright employed him as assistant and as Manager of the Dayton factory. In 1914 he was appointed Chief Aeronautical Engineer of the U.S. Army's Aviation Section in San Diego.

In 1915 Loening published his second book, "Military Aeroplanes," an Armyadopted text which was later officially used by the Royal Air Force, the U.S. Navy, the Canadian armed forces and others. In the same year he became Vice-President of the Sturtevant Aeroplane Company, where he pioneered the first American steel frame airplane. In 1917 he formed the Loening Aeronautical Engineering Corporation to work on a Navy contract for a small plane to be launched from destroyers, and an Army contract for the M-8 two-seat Pursuit monoplane embodying the pioneer use of rigid strut bracing, patented by Leoning.

After the war, Loening produced the Flying Yacht, a five-seat monoplane boat which established world records and opened up the first significant market for private aircraft. For this he received the Collier Trophy for 1921. His next success was the pioneer Loening Amphibian, with the first practical retractable undercarriage, used by the U.S. Army, Navy, Marines, and Coast Guard, and by airlines and private owners all over the world. Among its achievements was the Army's famous Pan-American Good Will Flight of 1926.

The Loening Aeronautical Engineering Corporation merged with the Curtiss-Wright Corporation in 1928, and Loening subsequently formed the Grover Loening Aircraft Company, building several research aircraft and establishing his first consulting engineering practice.

His third book, "Our Wings Grow Faster," was published in 1935. He entered public service in 1937 as aircraft advisor to the Maritime Commission, and in 1942 to the War Production Board. He became head consultant for the NACA in 1945, and received numerous other government assignments.

When the National Air Museum was founded in 1948, President Truman appointed him as the first of two civilian members of its Advisory Board, an appointment twice renewed by Presidents Eisenhower and Kennedy. He was awarded the Medal for Merit in 1946, the Eggleston Medal of Columbia University in 1949, the Wright Memorial Trophy in 1950, and the Air Force Medal in 1955.

MEDALIST FOR 1961

For his lifelong dedication to the cause of flight safety and his constant and untiring efforts to reduce the hazards of aviation.

JEROME LEDERER

Aviation safety is invisible and intangible, and of vital importance. Jerome Lederer made it his life's business, for which aviation can be duly thankful. He was born in New York City on September 26, 1902, and attended New York University, graduating in 1924 from the newly instituted aviation curriculum. Remaining at NYU as Assistant to the Director of Aeronautics of the College of Engineering, he received the degree of M.E. in 1925.

There being few positions in aviation available at that time, Lederer accepted a job on the West Shore Railroad as a surveyor. Soon afterward he became head of an engineering department of the U.S. Air Mail Service, where he developed specifications, tested parts, and examined wrecks to determine whether damaged aircraft could be repaired. In 1929 he became Chief Engineer of Aero Insurance Underwriters, in charge of loss prevention and safety.

President Roosevelt in 1940 reorganized the Civil Aeronautics Authority, consolidating its functions with those of the Civil Aeronautics Board. Lederer was asked to head up the Safety Bureau of the CAB. In World War II he was named Director of the Airlines War Training Institute, and there developed a program in which 10,000 pilots and mechanics were trained for the Air Transport Command. He returned to Aero Insurance Underwriters, but was soon called to serve as Consulting Operations Analyst for the U.S. Army Air Forces and later as a bombing research analyst with the U.S. Strategic Bombing Survey.

In 1947, at the request of airlines engineers and executives, he set up an aviation safety information service, which later became the Flight Safety Foundation, at the offices of the Institute of the Aeronautical Sciences. In 1948, aided by Laurance Rockefeller and others, it began to attract solid support. In addition to disseminating information on current operational problems relating to safety, this non-profit organization soon entered the field of research, undertaking a study for the Federal Aviation Agency on medical requirements for airmen, and a contract with the National Institutes of Health for studies of safety in private flying. In 1959 it took over from Cornell University the Aviation Crash Injury Project (AVCIR) at Phoenix, Arizona.

In 1950 the Cornell-Guggenheim Aviation Safety Center was established by The Daniel and Florence Guggenheim Foundation, and Lederer was asked to become its Director. He now heads this organization as well as the Flight Safety Foundation, the operations of which complement each other.

Lederer also serves on numerous governmental committees. He was a member of the Aviation Facilities Survey Group of the Bureau of the Budget; served with the Jet Task Force of the International Civil Aviation Organization; was a member of President Kennedy's Task Force on National Aviation Goals, and of the Research Advisory Committee on Aircraft Operating Problems of the National Aeronautics and Space Administration.

MEDALIST FOR 1962
(Posthumous)

*For technical and industrial leader-
ship in producing excellent aircraft
and space equipment, from early
fighters to the X-15 space plane.*

JAMES HOWARD KINDELBERGER

James Howard Kindelberger, known to all his friends as "Dutch", built more planes
during his lifetime than any other man in history. Born in Wheeling, West Virginia,
on May 8, 1895, he was forced to quit high school upon the death of his father in
order to support his family. He continued to study at night, and in 1913 became a
junior draftsman with the United States Army Corps of Engineers. Later he entered
Carnegie Institute of Technology, but during World War I left to enlist and serve as a
pilot and instructor in the Army Signal Corps.

He started his professional career as chief draftsman for the Glenn L. Martin
Company in Cleveland. In 1925 he became Chief Engineer of the Douglas Aircraft
Company. There he engineered the basic design that became the DC-1, followed by
the DC-2 and DC-3. In 1934 he took over as President and General Manager of
General Aviation Manufacturing Corporation, which presently became North Amer-

ican Aviation. He moved the company from Maryland to Los Angeles, and there built airplanes widely recognized by pilots as a pleasure to fly.

After a tour of Nazi Germany in 1938, he warned England of the Luftwaffe's rising might. In the war that followed, his own company's aircraft played a major role. Having started with a BT-9 trainer in the mid-1930's, North American built 15,400 T-6 Texan trainers during the war. More pilots learned to fly on the T-6 than on any other airplane. He and his staff completed the first P-51 Mustang in 127 days. Then came the B-25 Billy Mitchell bomber, used by General Doolittle on the first raid on Tokyo, and in every subsequent theater of World War II. By the end of the war, North American had built more airplanes than any other company in the world.

As airplane orders dwindled after the war, North American entered the missile, electronics, and atomic energy fields. The company led the industry in the development and manufacture of liquid rocket engines. North American pioneered in the field of inertial navigation, and provided the equipment that steered the first atomic submarines under the polar ice cap.

"Dutch" also kept his company in the front ranks in the airplane field, producing the first jet fighter for the Navy, the FJ-1, followed by the first four-jet bomber for the Air Force, the B-45 (Tornado). When the Korean War started, North American's F-86 Sabre Jet assured air superiority to the Allies by defeating the Russian-built MIGs. The F-100 Super Sabre succeeded the F-86 and became the first operational supersonic aircraft. The A3J Mach 2 Navy attack bomber and the X-15 supersonic aircraft, holder of world altitude and speed records, followed. The XB-70 Mach 3 supersonic Valkyrie was his last contribution to the field of aeronautics.

"Dutch" became Chief Executive Officer and Chairman of the Board of North American in 1948. He continued as Chief Executive Officer until 1960, and was Chairman of the Board until his death, July 27, 1962.

MEDALIST FOR 1963

For lifetime contribution of outstanding nature in the design and development of military aircraft, and for pioneer work in space technology.

JAMES SMITH McDONNELL

James Smith McDonnell early in life decided to become a builder of aircraft of his own design. The result has been a long series of major contributions to aircraft development, and to space flight advancement as well.

Born April 9, 1899, in Denver, Colorado, he entered Princeton University in 1917 and was graduated in 1921 with the degree of Bachelor of Science. He entered Massachusetts Institute of Technology to study aeronautical engineering, and at the same time applied for admission to the Army Air Corps Flying School in San Antonio, Texas, where he learned to fly. He received his Master's degree from MIT in 1925.

He began his aeronautical career as a test pilot with the Huff-Daland Aircraft Company. In late 1924 he joined Consolidated Aircraft Company in Buffalo, New York, as stress analyst and draftsman. A year later he became assistant chief engineer of the

Stout Metal Airplane Company, and in 1926 chief engineer of Hamilton-Aero Manufacturing Company.

In 1928 he formed McDonnell and Associates in Chicago to design and build a small monoplane for the Guggenheim Safe Aircraft Competition. The plane, *The Doodlebug*, performed well on flight tests, but the engine failed twice during preliminary trials, putting the plane out of the Competition. He repaired it later and used it successfully in a barnstorming tour.

In 1933 he joined the Glenn L. Martin Company, where he became chief project engineer for land planes. In 1938 he organized McDonnell Aircraft Corporation, in St. Louis, Missouri. Within a few months McDonnell had boldly entered an Army Air Corps design competition for a bomber-destroyer airplane. The bid led to research and development contracts, and the eventual purchase of a small factory.

In 1943 McDonnell Aircraft received its big opportunity: an invitation from the Navy to develop a jet fighter that could operate from an aircraft carrier. By the war's end the company had not only designed and built a successful carrier-based jet fighter, but also a pilotless aircraft missile, and the world's first twin-engine helicopter. Subsequently, the company built 800 F-2 Banshees and 500 F-3 Demons for the Navy, and 800 F-101 Voodoos for the Air Force. In 1958 it won a competition for the F-4 Phantom II Navy fighter, later manufacturing this aircraft for the Air Force as well. It produced the Air Force's Quail missile and the airframe and propulsion units for the Navy's Talos Missile.

In 1959 McDonnell Aircraft was selected to design, develop, and construct the first U.S. manned spacecraft for the National Aeronautics and Space Administration's Project Mercury. It subsequently received a contract to build the two-man Gemini spacecraft for NASA. Its ASSET glide re-entry vehicle for the Air Force was successfully flown in September 1963.

Printed in the Netherlands by
Joh. Enschedé en Zonen
Grafische Inrichting N.V. ⁄ Haarlem